PROTE

THE PGP USER'S GUIDE

William Stallings

Prentice Hall PTR
Englewood Cliffs, New Jersey 07632

Library of Congress Cataloging-in-Publication Data

Stallings, William
    Protect your privacy: the PGP user's guide/William Stallings.
        p.   cm.
    Includes index.
    ISBN 0-13-185596-4 (paper cover: alk. paper)
      1. PGP (Computer file) 2. Telecommunication systems—Security measures—
Data processiong. 3. Electronic mail systems—Security measures—Data processing.
4. Cryptography. I. Title.
TK5102.85.S73 1995   94–41526
005.8'2—dc20   CIP

Acquisitions Editor: *Paul W. Becker*
Cover Illustration: *David Tillinghast*
Cover Designer: *Deluca Design*
Manufacturing Manager: *Alexis R. Heydt*
Compositor/Production Service: *Digital Communications Services*

The publisher offers discounts on this book when ordered in bulk
quantities. For more information, contact Corporate Sales Department,
Prentice Hall PTR, 113 Sylvan Avenue, Englewood Cliffs, NJ 07632.
Phone: 800-382-3419; Fax: 201-592-2249; e-mail: dan_rush@prenhall.com

Printed in the United States of America
10 9 8 7 6 5 4 3 2 1

ISBN 0-13-185596-4

Prentice-Hall International (UK) Limited, *London*
Prentice-Hall of Australia Pty. Limited, *Sydney*
Prentice-Hall of Canada Inc., *Toronto*
Prentice-Hall Hispanoamericana S.A., *Mexico*
Prentice-Hall of India Private Limited, *New Delhi*
Prentice-Hall of Japan, Inc., *Tokyo*
Simon & Schuster Asia Pte. Ltd., *Singapore*
Editora Prentice-Hall do Brasil, Ltda., *Rio de Janeiro*

*For Tricia, of course
and Geoffroi too*

Contents

Foreword

by Philip Zimmermann

This book is about Pretty Good Privacy, a program I created to encrypt e-mail using public key cryptography. PGP was electronically published as free software in 1991. Little did I realize what this project would lead to. PGP has become the worldwide de facto standard for e-mail encryption.

I've admired Bill Stallings' writings in computer science for some years before PGP, and here he is writing a book about my program. How can I talk about how great his book is, without, by implication, talking about how great PGP is? It's hard to write a foreword for his book about PGP without sliding into some measure of self-indulgence.

I've been so close to this project for so long that I sometimes lose sight of the scope of what PGP provides. I got the manuscript for Bill's book in the mail the other day — the book you are holding. Sitting down with it, flipping through it, endless pages of diagrams, the formal treatment of it, services provided by PGP. It wasn't till I saw his book on PGP that I could step back and see PGP as others see it. The breadth of it. As a software engineer, I'm

used to either documenting my own software, or having a random
company tech writer document it. All software engineers get that.
But having William Stallings do the manual for your software —
it's sort of like having your portrait done by a world-class artist.
There are a very small number of software packages that
have far-reaching political implications. Most software that fits in
such an influential category has negative effects on our civil liberties. For example, government intelligence agencies use a software
package called PROMIS, which is a powerful tool of governments
to track people's activities, movements, spending, political affilia-
tions, et cetera. Now that is a piece of software with far-reaching
political implications. Mostly bad ones. Then there is the software
that the Medical Information Bureau uses to classify people who
file medical insurance claims, to put them on a medical "black list,"
so that they cannot purchase any medical insurance ever again.
That software has far-reaching political implications — enough to
raise a large-scale backlash in our society to do something about it.
In most cases, it seems that software that has powerful political
effects is software designed to strengthen the strong and weaken
the weak.

But PGP also has far-reaching political implications. Mostly
good ones. In the Information Age, cryptography affects the power
relationship between government and its people. The Government
knows this all too well, as evidenced by their recent policy initia-
tives for the Clipper chip, which would give the Government a
back door into all our private communications — an Orwellian
"wiretap chip" built into all our telephones, fax machines and computer networks. PGP strikes a blow against such dark trends, and
has become a crystal nucleus for the growth of the Crypto
Revolution, a new political movement for privacy and civil liberties
in the Information Age. This government has done all they can to
stop the emergence of a worldwide encryption standard that they
don't have a back door into. And that same government has placed
me under criminal investigation for unleashing this free software
on the world. If indicted and convicted, I would face 41 to 51
months in a federal prison.

Despite the pressure the Government has brought to bear
against PGP (or perhaps because of it), PGP has become the most
widely used software in the world for e-mail encryption, used by a

variety of activists, and anyone else needing protection from the powerful. It's also used by ordinary people to protect their personal and business communications from prying eyes.

PGP may have a future as an official Internet standard, as the Internet Engineering Task Force develops an interest in it. No one who wants to work in the area of Internet e-mail privacy should neglect studying PGP. Because of the "fax machine effect," more people who want to encrypt their e-mail are getting PGP because everyone else who encrypts their e-mail is already using it.

Naturally, I want people to read the Official PGP User's Guide, which comes with the electronic distribution package of PGP (also in book form from MIT Press), because I wrote it. Also, I'm more entertaining and personable in my book. And more political. But Bill Stallings' book is more comprehensive than mine, more thorough, covering more detail, with a lot more diagrams. He's really good at completely nailing it down in a book. In fact, I'll probably use his book myself as my preferred reference to PGP.

Philip Zimmermann
Boulder, Colorado
PGP Fingerprint:
9E 94 45 13 39 83 5F 70
7B E7 D8 ED C4 BE 5A A6

Acknowledgments

$\mathbf{M}$any people, including PGP beginners, experienced PGP users, and PGP developers, have given generously of their time and expertise to make this User's Guide a reality.

James Clough, Constantine Dokolas, Laurie Hanson, Michael Paul Johnson, Greg Louis, and Alicia Solomon reviewed the entire manuscript and provided many helpful comments and suggestions. Eric Allen, Matt Cowles, and Zig Fiedorowicz reviewed the material on MacPGP. They, as well as the mysterious "Xenon," provided useful insights into the Macintosh version of PGP. Dave Barnhart and the technical staff at ViaCrypt promptly answered many technical questions. Chris Geib, Ross Barclay, and James Still provided advice and review for WinPGP, PGP WinFront, and PGPShell respectively.

Joseph Christie, Steve Coltrin, Damien Doligez, Harald Fuchs, Mark Henderson, Jeremiah Junken, Roland Lipovits, Colin Plumb, "The Possum," and Dean Ridgway all provided useful "tips" which enhanced the value of the book.

Finally, this book would not have been possible without Phil

Zimmermann, not only because he is the creator of PGP, but because of his generous assistance to me personally. Through numerous telephone calls and e-mail exchanges, he has helped me develop an understanding of the technical internals of PGP and the trust model that is at the heart of PGP. To say the least, he is a Pretty Good Phil.

William Stallings

PGP Fingerprint:

B1 4E 2A BD 96 08 8B A4

67 83 D1 09 FE 52 56 6C

Reader's Guide to this PGP User's Guide

This book is for the users of PGP. It provides enough technical background on encryption, digital signatures, and related issues so that you can understand what PGP does. The focus here is on how to use PGP to achieve privacy in electronic correspondence and locally stored files. This book is therefore intended for the broad range of users who have access to a freeware version of PGP (including 3.0) or who have purchased the commercial version.

A PGP user's guide is needed even for those users who are reasonably sophisticated in the area of network security. The ways in which keys are managed and in which secure communication is established between two remote users are by no means obvious or simple. Some of the material in this book may be elementary. However, enough vital information is included to attract even the sophisticated user.

For you to make the best use of this book, I suggest reading the Introduction (Chapter 1) first, and then following the tailored advice in this section.

IF YOU HAVE ALREADY USED PGP

If you already have some experience, however limited, with PGP, then I suggest you read Part I first. This will deepen your understanding of how PGP works and clarify the important and complex concepts of key management.

In Part II, if you are using DOS PGP or UNIX PGP, you can skip Chapter 7 (DOS PGP: Getting Started) and go directly to Chapter 8 (DOS PGP Reference). Chapter 8 is a reference to which you will want to return later on, but it is worth reading straight through to begin with. There are numerous features of DOS PGP that are not specified in the documentation that comes with the package. I have tried to capture all of these undocumented features as well as, of course, the documented ones.

The same advice applies to Macintosh users. You can skip Chapter 9 and go directly to Chapter 10, reading it carefully and then referring back to it for reference.

Finally, if you have Windows for DOS, you may wish to take advantage of the convenience and user-friendliness of this interface. A number of Windows front-ends to DOS PGP exist. In Chapter 11 I discuss two quite different packages to give you a feel for what is available.

IF YOU HAVE NEVER USED PGP

If you have never used PGP, it might help to get a little experience with the package before trying to understand all of the underlying principles. For DOS or UNIX users, Chapter 7 provides step-by-step instructions for getting started, and Chapter 9 does the same for Macintosh users. Start with one of these chapters and go through all of the exercises, which should only take about 30 minutes or so. After that, you can go back to Part I and pick up from there.

SUPPLEMENTAL INFORMATION

In a nutshell, Part I provides a description of the principles of PGP, and Part II is a reference on how to use PGP. In addition, in Part III, there is some other important information that you may wish to refer to later.

Chapter 12 goes into some detail about the three principal' algorithms that are the building blocks of PGP: IDEA, RSA, and MD5. While you don't need to know the details of these algorithms to use PGP, a basic knowledge of their strengths will increase your confidence in PGP.

One very important aspect of PGP is the choice of a passphrase. Picking a secure passphrase is not as easy as many people think. If your passphrase is easily guessed, then PGP's elaborate security is compromised. For this reason, Chapter 13, on choosing a passphrase, is worth careful study.

Most versions of PGP are freely available on the Internet or bulletin board systems. Chapter 14 provides a list of access points that was current at the time of publication.

Many users of PGP will want to take advantage of a free service known as the public key server. Chapter 15 provides a guide to the use of key servers and lists some of the servers available at the time of publication.

A final word: The Official PGP User's Guide, soon to be available in book form from MIT Press, and now available in electronic form with the electronic distribution package of PGP, is well worth reading. It provides a powerful case for the need for PGP and presents Phil Zimmermann's thoughts on the design and philosophy of PGP.

Protect Your Privacy!

When you write a personal letter to your doctor, lawyer, or lover, do you use a postcard? When you mail important documents to your accountant or business colleague, do you leave the envelope unsealed?

Few people would answer yes to such questions. You expect privacy when you use the postal service and you take steps to ensure it by sending letters and documents in sealed envelopes. Why? Because a letter is going to pass through a number of hands before it reaches its intended recipient, so the use of sealed envelopes is an obvious precaution. Yet millions of people use electronic mail for all kinds of messages and documents without giving a thought to privacy.

But you should think about e-mail privacy. A message sent over the Internet can pass through dozens of mail forwarders and packet-switching nodes. A system administrator or someone with privileged access to any of these transfer points is in a position to read those messages. And it gets worse: It isn't all that difficult to spoof the network into sending e-mail with an incorrect return address, enabling impersonation. It is also not that difficult to intercept a message, alter its contents, and then send it on its way.

What can you do? If you are just using e-mail within a closed company environment and everyone is using the same package, then there are a number of products, such as Lotus Notes, that support e-mail privacy services. But, if you want to use the Internet or a commercial service such as Compuserve to send messages to others, whether they are using DOS, Windows, Macintosh, UNIX, or whatever, then one choice stands out: Pretty Good Privacy (PGP).

1.1 WHAT IS PGP?

The Origins of PGP

PGP is a remarkable phenomenon. Largely the creation of a single person, Phil Zimmermann, PGP provides confidentiality and authentication services for electronic mail and file storage applications. In essence Zimmermann has done the following:

1. Selected the best available cryptographic algorithms as building blocks.
2. Integrated these algorithms into a general-purpose application independent of operating system or processor, based on a small set of easy-to-use commands.
3. Made the package and its documentation, including the source code, freely available via the Internet, bulletin boards, and commercial networks such as Compuserve.
4. Entered into an agreement with the company ViaCrypt to provide a fully compatible, low-cost commercial version of PGP.

Since its introduction in 1991, use of PGP has grown explosively and is now widespread. A number of reasons can be cited for this growth:

1. PGP is available free worldwide in versions that run on a variety of platforms including DOS/Windows, UNIX, Macintosh, and many more. In addition, the commercial version satisfies users who want vendor support.
2. It is based on algorithms that have survived extensive public review and are considered extremely secure. Specifically, the package includes RSA for public-key encryption, IDEA for conventional encryption, and MD5 for hash coding.
3. It has a wide range of applicability, from corporations that want to enforce a standardized scheme for file and message

encryption to individuals who wish to communicate securely over the Internet and other networks.

4. It wasn't developed by, nor is it controlled by, any governmental or standards organization. For those with an
instinctive distrust of "the establishment," this makes PGP
attractive.

What PGP Does

PGP provides two services: encryption and authentication by
means of a digital signature. The encryption service allows a user
to encrypt a file either for storage or transmission as an e-mail
message. The storage option is handy if you wish to store a file but
are worried about others gaining access to it. The e-mail option is,
of course, the feature that enables PGP to be used for private
exchanges over a network. PGP encrypts the entire contents of the
message in such a way that only the intended recipient can decrypt and read the message. Anyone intercepting the message will
be get a meaningless garble.

The authentication service allows a user to digitally sign a
document before transmission. This is done in such a way that (1)
anyone can verify that the document has not been changed since it
was signed, that is, if someone alters the message or substitutes a
different message, the signature will no longer be valid; and (2)
anyone can verify that the message has been signed by a particular individual, preventing impersonation.

1.2 PGP VERSIONS

Until the early part of 1994, life was fairly simple for the PGP
user. The common denominator for all users was PGP version 2.3,
available at a number of Internet ftp sites, through a number of
commercial on-line services, such as Compuserve, and on numerous bulletin boards worldwide. Outside the U.S., there were no
legal difficulties in using PGP. Inside the U.S., PGP 2.3 faced a
legal problem. The package includes the RSA algorithm, for which
there is a valid U.S. patent. Thus, any user of PGP 2.3 in the U.S.
was vulnerable to being accused of patent infringement. One solution to this problem was the use of ViaCrypt PGP 2.4. ViaCrypt is
a company that sells a supported version of PGP and has a subli-

cense from the RSA patent holder. For the U.S. user willing to pay for PGP, PGP 2.4 was available and fully interoperable with PGP 2.3.

But complications arose. In May of 1994, a group at MIT sanctioned by Phil Zimmermann issued a freeware version of PGP known as PGP 2.6. This version was released for noncommercial use with the agreement of the RSA patent holder and can therefore be used in the U.S. without risk of patent infringement. One problem with PGP 2.6 is that, since it was developed and deployed in the U.S., it cannot be legally exported without an export license. However, PGP 2.6 quickly found its way outside the U.S., and there is nothing illegal about using the exported version; it was only illegal to export it. Another problem with 2.6 is that it doesn't fully interoperate with 2.3 and 2.4. PGP will decrypt messages and use keys generated by PGP 2.3 and 2.4. However, these earlier versions are unable to decrypt messages and use keys generated by PGP 2.6. MIT says that the reason for this incompatibility is to discourage use of the earlier software and mitigate the patent-caused problems that have hampered use of PGP within the U.S.

Several significant developments have occurred since the introduction of PGP 2.6. Viacrypt has upgraded its products to Version 2.7, which is compatible with and interoperable with 2.6, 2.4 and 2.3.

For users outside the U.S. and Canada, yet another freeware version has been developed in the U.K., known as PGP 2.6ui. The "ui" stands for Unofficial International release because, unlike version 2.6, it hasn't been approved by Phil Zimmermann. Nevertheless, it is gaining in popularity. Thus, users outside the U.S. and Canada have two options, which should be compatible with each other.

The user thus has a number of choices. One likely question is: how safe are the various versions? That is, is there any sort of back door in any implementation that could be used by someone in the know to break the system? The developers of all these versions naturally assert that this isn't the case. For all freeware versions, the source code as well as the object code is available so that anyone can verify its integrity. For legal reasons, ViaCrypt doesn't provide source code, but the security of their version is endorsed by Phil Zimmermann. The personal opinion of the author is that

all of these versions are safe, but you must make up your own
mind. What I can say is that PGP has attracted a large and devoted following, including many individuals and organizations such
as the Electronic Frontier Foundation, among those who have a
keen distrust of governmental and organizational attempts to
invade privacy. The size of PGP's user base is a testimony to its
security.

Finally, as this book went to press, PGP 3.0 was in the plan-
ning stages. This version, like PGP 2.6, will have patent approval
and will be available worldwide. Although it will add new features
to PGP, it will be compatible with PGP 2.6 and use the same command set and format, with additions.

HOW PGP WORKS

2

Basic Principles of PGP

$$\text{B}_{\text{efore}}$$ we launch into PGP, you need to know something about the basic building blocks of PGP. You don't need to become an expert in this area, but you do need to know enough about these algorithms to:

- Assess for yourself the strength of PGP
- Understand the importance of "key size"
- Appreciate the need for key management techniques to supplement PGP
- Know what you must do to ensure the privacy and authenticity of messages you send and receive with PGP

It turns out that it isn't all that easy to (1) develop algorithms that cannot be defeated even by a determined opponent and (2) put those algorithms together into a practical system that provides security and authenticity. The building blocks of PGP represent the culmination of years of research and development in the field of cryptography, and PGP itself builds on years of development and analysis of security applications.

We start with conventional encryption, which PGP uses to provide confidentiality. With confidentiality, an eavesdropper will be unable to read messages scrambled using conventional encryption.

Next we move to a remarkable technique known as public-key encryption. Although this is also a type of encryption algorithm, it isn't practical for use in scrambling messages. Instead

PGP uses it to transfer the key of the conventional algorithm and to produce a digital signature (don't worry if these terms mean nothing: all will become clear later in this chapter).

The final concept dealt with in this chapter, the secure hash function, is vital to the digital signature process.

This chapter only discusses the basic principles underlying PGP, and doesn't go into the details of the specific algorithms used in PGP. These algorithms are:

- For conventional encryption, PGP uses IDEA, which is believed to be one of the strongest conventional encryption algorithms available.
- For public key encryption, PGP uses RSA, the only widely-accepted algorithm in this category.
- For a secure hash function, PGP uses MD5, which is considered to be a very strong example of this type of function.

Chapter 12 provides an overview of each of these algorithms.

FURTHER READING

To gain an appreciation of the difficulty of "getting things right," read The Codebreakers: The Story of Secret Writing, by David Kahn (Macmillan/Prentice-Hall, 1967). An abridged edition leaves out some of the more technical narrative but captures the true drama of this book (New American Library, 1974). A key theme in the book is that, time and again, cryptographers have come up with a scheme considered to be virtually unbreakable only to find later that there was some clever way to attack it. This book is a landmark that brought a legion of bright civilians into the field, including Whitfield Diffie, who first announced the concept of public-key cryptography. Another interesting look into the making and breaking of codes is The Puzzle Palace by James Bamford (Penguin Books, 1983), which examines the super-secret National Security Agency.

2.1 CONVENTIONAL ENCRYPTION

Conventional encryption, also referred to as symmetric encryption or single-key encryption, was the only type of encryption in use prior to the introduction of public-key encryption in the late

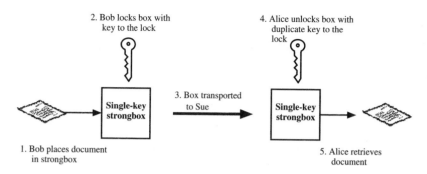

Fig 2.1   Strongbox with Keyhole Lock

1970's. This type of encryption has been used for secret communication by countless individuals and groups, from Julius Caesar to the German U-boat force to present-day diplomatic, military, and commercial users. It remains by far the more widely used of the two types of encryption.

A useful analogy to conventional encryption is a strongbox with a single lock and two copies of the key (Figure 2.1). Say Bob wants to send a secure message to Alice and suppose that Bob and Alice each have one of the two keys. Bob places the message in the strongbox and locks it with his copy of the key. The strongbox is then transported to Alice. Anyone can be trusted to do the transporting, since the box is locked. When Alice gets the box, she unlocks it, using her copy of the key.

For this scheme to work, there are two requirements:

1. We need a box with a good, strong lock on it. The lock corresponds to the encryption algorithm: It protects the message from disclosure.

2. Alice and Bob must have obtained copies of the key to that lock in a secure fashion and must keep the keys secure. If someone can temporarily get hold of one of the keys, that person can make a duplicate.

Is this system secure? We have to look at what an opponent can do. There are two methods of attack. The opponent can try to force or pick the lock, perhaps with a crowbar or a lock pick.

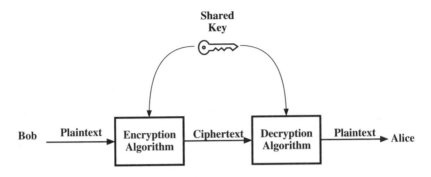

Fig 2.2   Conventional Encryption

Whether or not this method works is related to the "strength" of the lock, that is, how well it resists such attacks. There is also another way: Knowing the size of the keyhole in the lock, an opponent could manufacturer all possible keys of that size, with one key for each possible key shape. Then the opponent can try every key until one fits the lock. Whether or not this method works depends on how many such keys there are and how long it takes to test each key. For example, if there are only 10,000 possible key shapes and it takes 5 seconds to test each key, then the bad guy could run through all the keys in 50,000 seconds, about 14 hours.

Now let us look at conventional encryption. Again, Bob wants to send a message to Alice in such a way that no one else except Alice can read the message (Figure 2.2). The original message is referred to as *plaintext*. To thwart potential eavesdroppers, Bob scrambles the message using an encryption algorithm, producing ciphertext. Anyone reading the *ciphertext* would see an apparently random string of nonsense. Now, the specific content of the ciphertext depends not only on the algorithm but also on a key. The key is a value independent of the plaintext that controls the algorithm. For this scheme to work, the key must be kept secret, known only to Bob and Alice, and so we shall call this a *secret key*. The algorithm will produce a different output depending on the specific key being used at the time. That is, changing the key changes the output of the algorithm.

Once the ciphertext is produced, Bob transmits the message to Alice. Alice can then transform the ciphertext back to the origi-

nal plaintext by using a reverse version of the same algorithm with the same key that Bob used.
Recalling the two requirements for communication by lock-box, there are two analogous requirements for communication by conventional encryption:

1. We need a strong encryption algorithm. At a minimum, we would like the algorithm to be such that an opponent who knows the algorithm and has access to one or more cipher-texts would be unable to decipher the ciphertext or figure out the key. This requirement is usually stated in a stronger form: The opponent should be unable to decrypt ciphertext or discover the key even if he or she is in posses-sion of a number of ciphertexts together with the plaintext that produced each ciphertext.
2. Alice and Bob must have obtained copies of the secret key in a secure fashion and must keep the key secure. If some-one can discover the key and knows the algorithm, all com-munication using this key is readable.

Again, as in the case of the locked strongbox, there are two general approaches to attacking a conventional encryption scheme. The first attack is known as cryptanalysis. Cryptanalytic attacks rely on the nature of the algorithm plus perhaps some knowledge of the general characteristics of the plaintext or even some sample plaintext-ciphertext pairs. This type of attack exploits the charac-teristics of the algorithm to attempt to deduce a specific plaintext or to deduce the key being used. Of course, if the attack succeeds in deducing the key, the effect is catastrophic: All future and past messages encrypted with that key are compromised.
The second method, known as the brute-force attack, is to try every possible key on a piece of ciphertext until an intelligible translation into plaintext is obtained. On average, half of all possi-ble keys must be tried to achieve success. Table 2.1 shows how much time is involved for various key sizes. The table shows results for each key size, assuming that it takes 1 microsecond to perform a single decryption, a reasonable order of magnitude for today's computers. With the use of massively parallel organiza-tions of microprocessors, it may be possible to achieve processing

rates many orders of magnitude greater. The final column of the table considers the results for a system that can process 1 million keys per microsecond. As one can see, at this performance level, a 56-bit key can no longer be considered computationally secure.

Table **2.1**

Average Time Required for Exhaustive Key Search

Key Size	Number of Alternative Keys	Time required at 1 encryption/μs	Time required at 10^6 encryptions/μs
32 bits	$2^{32} = 4.3 \times 10^9$	2^{31} μs = 35.8 minutes	2.15 milliseconds
56 bits	$2^{56} = 7.2 \times 10^{16}$	2^{55} μs = 1142 years	10.01 hours
128 bits	$2^{128} = 3.4 \times 10^{38}$	2^{127} μs = 5.4×10^{24} years	5.4×10^{18} years

PGP makes use of the IDEA encryption algorithm, which takes a 128-bit key.

2.2 PUBLIC-KEY ENCRYPTION

Public-key encryption, first publicly proposed by Diffie and Hellman in 1976, is the first truly revolutionary advance in encryption in literally thousands of years. For one thing, public-key algorithms are based on mathematical functions rather than on simple operations on bit patterns. More importantly, public-key cryptography is asymmetric, involving the use of two separate keys, in contrast to the symmetric conventional encryption, which uses only one key. The use of two keys has profound consequences in the areas of confidentiality, key distribution, and authentication.

Before proceeding, we should first mention several common misconceptions concerning public-key encryption. One such misconception is that public-key encryption is more secure from cryptanalysis than conventional encryption. In fact, the security of any encryption scheme depends on the length of the key and the computational work involved in breaking a cipher. There is nothing in principle about either conventional or public-key encryption that makes one superior to another from the point of view of resisting

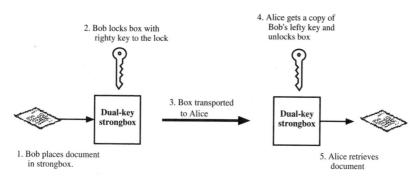

2. Bob locks box with
righty key to the lock

4. Alice gets a copy of
Bob's lefty key and
unlocks box

3. Box transported
to Alice

Dual-key strongbox

Dual-key strongbox

1. Bob places document
in strongbox.

5. Alice retrieves
document

Fig **2.3**   Strongbox with Dual-Key Lock

cryptanalysis. A second misconception is that public-key encryption is a general-purpose technique that has made conventional encryption obsolete. On the contrary, because of the computational overhead of current public-key encryption schemes, there seems no foreseeable likelihood that conventional encryption will be abandoned. Finally, there is a feeling that key distribution is trivial when using public-key encryption, compared to the rather cumbersome handshaking involved with key distribution centers for conventional encryption. In fact, some form of protocol is needed, often involving a central agent, and the procedures involved are no simpler nor any more efficient than those required for conventional encryption.

A useful analogy to public-key encryption is a strongbox with a special kind of lock that accommodates two types of keys (Figure 2.3). One key, a lefty key, turns the locking mechanism to the left and the other key, a righty key, turns it to the right. When the mechanism is unlocked, it is in a center position. If it is turned to either the left or the right, it is locked and the box cannot be opened. So an unlocked box can be locked with either a lefty key or a righty key; however, if the box is locked with a lefty key, the only way to unlock it is with a righty key and, similarly, if it is locked with a righty key, the only way to unlock it is with a lefty key.

Now, say that Bob wants to send a secure message to Alice and suppose that he has the righty key for a strongbox and Alice has the matching lefty key. Bob places the message in the strongbox and locks it with the righty key. The strongbox is then transported to Alice. Anyone can be trusted to do the transporting, since the box is locked. When Alice gets the box, she unlocks it using the lefty key.

This special kind of strongbox opens up all kinds of possibilities. For example, let us say that we have a community of people who want to exchange messages in strongboxes. Everyone in the group can buy their own personal strongbox with unique lefty and righty keys. Each member of the group maintains exclusive possession of his or her righty key but all lefty keys are shared. This could be done, for example, by having everyone write their name on their lefty key and depositing these keys with a locksmith. When anyone wants someone else's lefty key, they can go to the locksmith, who will duplicate the requested key. Furthermore, the locksmith, who made all the strongbox locks, has duplicates of all of the strongboxes in the community.

Consider the following scenario: Bob wants to send a message to Alice and make sure that no one but Alice can read it. Here's how: Bob gets a duplicate of Alice's lefty key and of her strongbox, puts the message in the box, and locks the box. Since only Alice has the righty key for this box, only she can open the box.

Another scenario: Bob wants to send a message to Alice and, although it isn't important that the message be kept secret, he wants Alice to be certain that the message is indeed from him. In this case Bob uses his own strongbox and locks it with his righty key. When Alice receives the box, she finds that she can open it with Bob's lefty key, thus proving that the box must have been locked by Bob.

Now let us look at public-key encryption. A general-purpose public-key cryptographic algorithm relies on one key for encryption and a different but related key for decryption. Furthermore, these algorithms have the following important characteristics:

- It is computationally infeasible to determine the decryption key given only knowledge of the cryptographic algorithm and the encryption key.
- Either of the two related keys can be used for encryption, with the other used for decryption.

The essential steps are the following:

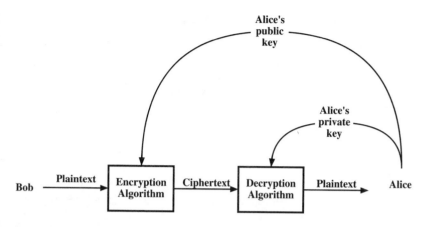

Fig **2.4**   Public-Key Encryption

1. Each user generates a pair of keys to be used for the encryption and decryption of messages.
2. Each user places one of the two keys in a public register or other accessible file. This is the public key. The companion key is kept private.
3. If Bob wishes to send a private message to Alice, Bob encrypts the message using Alice's public key.
4. When Alice receives the message, she decrypts it, using her private key. No other recipient can decrypt the message because only Alice knows her private key.

With this approach, all participants have access to public keys, and private keys are generated locally by each participant and therefore need never be distributed. As long as a user protects his or her private key, incoming communication is secure. At any time, a user can change the private key and publish the companion public key to replace the old public key.

Figure 2.4 illustrates the process of public-key encryption. Bob encrypts a plaintext message with Alice's public key, producing ciphertext. The ciphertext depends on the encryption algorithm and also on the key. When Alice receives the ciphertext, she can decrypt it using her private key.

PGP uses the public-key algorithm RSA.

What's the Advantage of Public-Key Encryption?

Compared to the typical conventional encryption algorithm, public-key encryption is painfully slow. So, what is the point of this new method? The answer is that public-key encryption provides us with tremendous flexibility to perform a number of security-related functions. Two areas in particular stand out: key management and authentication.

Key Management

With conventional encryption, a fundamental requirement for two parties to communicate securely is that they share a secret key. Suppose Bob wants to create a messaging application that will enable him to exchange e-mail securely with anyone who has access to the Internet or to some other network that the two of them share (e.g., an on-line service such as Compuserve). Suppose Bob wants to do this using only conventional encryption. With conventional encryption, Bob and his correspondent, say, Alice, must come up with a way to share of a unique secret key that no one else knows. How are they going to do that? If Alice is in the next room from Bob, Bob could generate a key and write it down on a piece of paper or store it on a diskette and hand it to Alice. But if Alice is on the other side of the continent or the world, what can Bob do? Well, he could encrypt this key using conventional encryption and e-mail it to Alice, but this means that Bob and Alice must share a secret key in order to encrypt this new secret key. Furthermore, Bob and everyone else who uses this new e-mail package faces the same problem with every potential correspondent: Each pair of correspondents must share a unique secret key.

How to distribute secret keys securely is the most difficult problem for conventional encryption. This problem is wiped away with public-key encryption by the simple fact that the private key is never distributed. If Bob wants to correspond with Alice and other people, he generates a single pair of keys, one private and one public. He keeps the private key secure and broadcasts the public key to all and sundry. If Alice does the same, then Bob has Alice's public key, Alice has Bob's public key, and they can now communicate securely.

It is only fair to point out, however, that we have replaced one problem with another. Bob's private key is secure since he need never reveal it; however, Alice must be sure that the public key with Bob's name written all over it is in fact Bob's public key. Someone else could have broadcast a public key and said it was Bob's. We explore a number of ways to overcome this problem when we discuss PGP in the following chapters.

Authentication

Suppose that Bob and Alice share a secret key for conventional encryption and that Alice receives an encrypted message that is allegedly from Bob. Alice decrypts the message and recovers intelligible plaintext. Conclusion: This is a genuine message from Bob, since Bob is the only person other than Alice who knows the shared secret key.

One weak spot in this arrangement is that Bob can send Alice a message and later deny it. What would be the point? Well, suppose Bob is an investor and Alice a broker. On Monday Bob sends Alice a message with instructions to buy a thousand shares of Speculative Unlimited. On Tuesday the stock drops 10 points on bad news. On Wednesday Bob gets a written confirmation of the Monday trade and promptly denies that he ever gave such instructions. Can Alice prove otherwise? No, because Alice could have easily generated the buy order, encrypted it with the key she shares with Bob, and then decrypted her own message!

Public-key encryption solves this problem. This time, let us say Bob sends a message to Alice encrypted with his private key. Alice decrypts the message, using Bob's public key, but also retains the encrypted version. If Bob later denies he sent the message, all Alice has to do is present a judge or other arbitrator with the ciphertext, the plaintext, and Bob's public key. The arbitrator can confirm that the ciphertext translates into the plaintext in question with Bob's public key, and that the ciphertext must therefore have been created by Bob with his private key. Case closed!

2.3 SECURE HASH FUNCTIONS

The scheme for authentication just described is impractical for the simple reason that public-key encryption of large blocks of data is painfully slow. We want to avoid having to encrypt thousands or tens of thousands or even millions of bits using RSA or a similar algorithm; it is just plain unwieldy. To get around this problem we may use a technique known as the digital signature. This scheme depends on not only public-key encryption but also another kind of algorithm known as a secure hash function.

Figure 2.5 illustrates the digital signature scheme. Bob has a message that needs to be authenticated. To do this with as little overhead as possible, Bob calculates a function of the text, called a message digest, or hash code. The purpose of the hash code is to produce a fingerprint for a message that is for all practical purposes unique to that message. Next Bob encrypts the hash code with his private key; the result is called a digital signature. Finally Bob attaches the digital signature to the message and sends the whole thing to Alice.

On Alice's end, she is presented with a message and a signature. This gives Alice the opportunity to verify that the message is from Bob. First Alice uses the same hash function that Bob used to calculate the hash code for this message. Alice sets this aside temporarily and turns to the signature. Using Bob's public key, Alice decrypts the signature to recover a hash code. Finally Alice compares the decrypted hash code with the one that she calculated; if there is a match, Alice can conclude that the message is from Bob and could only have come from Bob. Why? Well, let's look at the possibilities:

1. Suppose the bad guy (we'll call him BG) prepares a message and attempts to forge Bob's signature. BG can generate the hash code for the fraudulent message, but since BG doesn't know Bob's private key, BG cannot properly encrypt the message. So BG cannot forge Bob's signature.

2. Suppose instead that BG intercepts a message from Bob. Now he has a message and a signature. Can BG discard the message, create another message, and attach the stolen signature to this new message? No, because the new message will have a different hash code from the old message and therefore the hash code in the signature won't match the hash code of the message.

3. Again, suppose that BG intercepts the message, but this time he just makes a slight alteration to the message (e.g.,

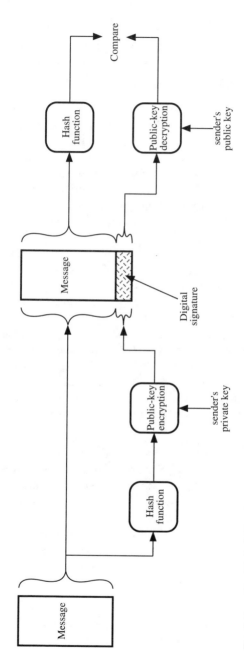

Fig **2.5**   The Digital Signature

inserting or deleting the word not in a critical place). Once again, this cannot succeed, because any change in the message will change the hash code and therefore result in a signature mismatch.

The digital signature is one of the great innovations in the history of cryptography. The recipient of a signed message knows that the message is in fact from the alleged source and that the message hasn't been altered in any way after it was signed. The digital signature makes possible a whole range of security services that are impractical using conventional encryption. We will see that PGP relies heavily on the use of digital signatures.

For the digital signature application, the hash function must have the following five properties:

1. It must work on messages of any size.
2. It must produce a hash code of fixed size.
3. It must be relatively easy to compute so that it is a practical means of authentication.
4. It must depend on the entire message so that it isn't possible to make any undetected alterations on a signed message.
5. It must be prohibitively difficult to invert the hashing process in the sense of being able to construct a message with a given hash code or of being able to construct two different messages that produce the same hash code.

Property 5 implies that the digest cannot be too short. For example, suppose we use an 8-bit digest. This means that there are only 256 possible digest values, so many messages must map into the same digest value.

How big should the digest be? Well, suppose we use a 32-bit digest. There will be 2^{32} different digests or over 4 billion different digests. Now suppose our old friend BG wants to send a fraudulent message to Alice. The message is as follows:

Dear Alice,

This message is to introduce you to Alfred Barton, the new senior jewelry buyer for our Northern European division. He has taken over responsibility for all our interests in watches and jewelry in the area. Please give him all the help he needs to find the most up to date lines for the high end of the market. He is authorized to receive on our behalf samples of the latest watch and jewelry products, subject to a limit of one hundred thousand dollars. He will carry a signed copy of this document as proof of identity. An order with his signature, which is attached, authorizes you to charge the cost to this company at the head office address. We expect that our volume of orders will increase in the next year and trust that the new appointment will prove advantageous to both our companies.

Sincerely,

Bob

BG captures a signed message from Bob, throws away the message and retains the signature. Using Bob's public key, BG decrypts the signature to recover the hash code. Now BG must make sure that his message has the same hash code. Since there are over 4 billion different possible hash codes, this seems pretty unlikely. But there are ways around that. For example, Figure 2.6 shows 2^{37} different variations on BG's message, all of which carry essentially the same meaning. With only 2^{32} different hash codes, and 2^{37} possible messages, all BG has to do is start running through the variations until a match is found. Bingo! BG takes his message and attaches Bob's signature and Alice will accept it.

Of course, running through that many possibilities will take a lot of time. The larger the hash code the longer the search time. Ultimately, we can make the hash code so large that this kind of stunt becomes infeasible. Current thinking is that a hash code of 128 bits is extremely secure.

PGP uses the secure hash function MD5, which produces a 128-bit hash code.

Dear Alice,

$\left\{ \begin{array}{l} \text{This message is} \\ \text{I am writing} \end{array} \right\}$ to introduce $\left\{ \begin{array}{l} \text{you to} \\ \text{to you} \end{array} \right\}$ $\left\{ \begin{array}{l} \text{Mr.} \\ \text{--} \end{array} \right\}$ Alfred $\left\{ \begin{array}{l} \text{P.} \\ \text{--} \end{array} \right\}$

Barton, the $\left\{ \begin{array}{l} \text{new} \\ \text{newly appointed} \end{array} \right\}$ $\left\{ \begin{array}{l} \text{chief} \\ \text{senior} \end{array} \right\}$ jewelry buyer for $\left\{ \begin{array}{l} \text{our} \\ \text{the} \end{array} \right\}$

Northern $\left\{ \begin{array}{l} \text{European} \\ \text{Europe} \end{array} \right\}$ $\left\{ \begin{array}{l} \text{area} \\ \text{division} \end{array} \right\}$. He $\left\{ \begin{array}{l} \text{will take} \\ \text{has taken} \end{array} \right\}$ over $\left\{ \begin{array}{l} \text{the} \\ \text{--} \end{array} \right\}$

responsibility for $\left\{ \begin{array}{l} \text{all} \\ \text{the whole of} \end{array} \right\}$ our interests in $\left\{ \begin{array}{l} \text{watches and jewelry} \\ \text{jewelry and watches} \end{array} \right\}$

in the $\left\{ \begin{array}{l} \text{area} \\ \text{region} \end{array} \right\}$. Please $\left\{ \begin{array}{l} \text{afford} \\ \text{give} \end{array} \right\}$ him $\left\{ \begin{array}{l} \text{every} \\ \text{all the} \end{array} \right\}$ help he $\left\{ \begin{array}{l} \text{may need} \\ \text{needs} \end{array} \right\}$

to $\left\{ \begin{array}{l} \text{seek out} \\ \text{find} \end{array} \right\}$ the most $\left\{ \begin{array}{l} \text{modern} \\ \text{up to date} \end{array} \right\}$ lines for the $\left\{ \begin{array}{l} \text{top} \\ \text{high} \end{array} \right\}$ end of the

market. He is $\left\{ \begin{array}{l} \text{empowered} \\ \text{authorized} \end{array} \right\}$ to receive on our behalf $\left\{ \begin{array}{l} \text{samples} \\ \text{specimens} \end{array} \right\}$ of the

$\left\{ \begin{array}{l} \text{latest} \\ \text{newest} \end{array} \right\}$ $\left\{ \begin{array}{l} \text{watch and jewelry} \\ \text{jewelry and watch} \end{array} \right\}$ products, $\left\{ \begin{array}{l} \text{up} \\ \text{subject} \end{array} \right\}$ to a $\left\{ \begin{array}{l} \text{limit} \\ \text{maximum} \end{array} \right\}$

of one hundred thousand dollars. He will $\left\{ \begin{array}{l} \text{carry} \\ \text{hold} \end{array} \right\}$ a signed copy of this $\left\{ \begin{array}{l} \text{letter} \\ \text{document} \end{array} \right\}$

as proof of identity. An order with his signature, which is $\left\{ \begin{array}{l} \text{appended} \\ \text{attached} \end{array} \right\}$

$\left\{ \begin{array}{l} \text{authorizes} \\ \text{allows} \end{array} \right\}$ you to charge the cost to this company at the $\left\{ \begin{array}{l} \text{headquarters} \\ \text{head office} \end{array} \right\}$

address. We $\left\{ \begin{array}{l} \text{fully} \\ \text{--} \end{array} \right\}$ expect that our $\left\{ \begin{array}{l} \text{level} \\ \text{volume} \end{array} \right\}$ of orders will increase in

the $\left\{ \begin{array}{l} \text{following} \\ \text{next} \end{array} \right\}$ year and $\left\{ \begin{array}{l} \text{trust} \\ \text{hope} \end{array} \right\}$ that the new appointment will $\left\{ \begin{array}{l} \text{be} \\ \text{prove} \end{array} \right\}$

$\left\{ \begin{array}{l} \text{advantageous} \\ \text{an advantage} \end{array} \right\}$ to both our companies.

Sincerely,

Bob

Fig **2.6**   A Fraudulent Letter in 2^{37} Variations. *(Reprinted from* Security for Computer Networks, Second Edition, *[Davies and Price], copyright 1989, by permission of John Wiley & Sons, Ltd.)*

Sending and Receiving PGP Messages

I n a nutshell, PGP provides two services for its users: confidentiality, by encrypting messages; and authentication, by providing digital signatures. When designing a secure e-mail application, such as PGP, that provides these services, the designer faces two main problems. First, how secure is the application? In the case of PGP, its services depend on three algorithms: IDEA (conventional encryption), RSA (public-key encryption), and MD5 (secure hash function). While no one can absolutely guarantee that these algorithms provide a given level of security, all three have been the subject of extensive analysis and it is widely believed that all three are extremely secure. No one can say that there might not someday be a breakthrough that would provide a feasible line of attack to one of these algorithms or, indeed, that some unpublished attack (e.g., developed by the U.S. National Security Agency) doesn't already exist. The author, however, shares the virtually unanimous opinion of those in this field that all three of these algorithms are, for all practical purposes, currently unbreakable.

There remains another design issue: How can these algorithms be packaged to produce a practical application for e-mail security? It turns out that one ends up with a rather complex package to do the job right, and, to use PGP effectively, one must understand, at least in general terms, how PGP supports confidentiality and authentication. Providing that understanding is the goal of this chapter.

We begin with an overall view of the steps performed by PGP

in preparing and transmitting messages and in receiving and processing messages. Then we look in more detail at each of the main steps in this process.

A CAUTIONARY TALE

To appreciate the difficulty in assuring that an algorithm is secure, it is worth pondering the experience of Ralph Merkle, who has been characterized by Whitfield Diffie as the single most inventive character in the public key cryptography saga. Early on, Merkle proposed a public-key encryption scheme known as the trapdoor knapsack. The general knapsack problem deals with determining which objects are in a container given only the total weight. Merkle showed how to turn this problem into a public-key system. The knapsack algorithm was hailed by many as an unbreakable system. Merkle, confident though not rich, offered a reward of $100 to anyone who could break it. It took four years for Adi Shamir, one of the inventors of RSA, to break the system and collect the $100. But Merkle wasn't through. He devised a way to make the hard knapsack problem even harder, and upped the stakes to $1000 for anyone who could break the revised scheme. This time he had to wait only two years before paying up. Later on, Merkle developed a secure hash algorithm called Snefru, which become quite popular on UNIX systems. Alas, an effective way of breaking this algorithm was also discovered. Fortunately, Merkle had not bet any money on this scheme.

3.1 PGP: THE BIG PICTURE

The actual operation of PGP for sending and receiving messages (as opposed to key management services, discussed in Chapter 6), consists of five services: digital signature, message encryption, compression, e-mail compatibility, and segmentation (Table 3.1). Figure 3.1 traces the progress of a message through PGP from sender to receiver and illustrates all of these services, except segmentation. Let us walk through the figure a step at a time.

Preparing the File

PGP takes as input a file stored somewhere on the computer system where PGP is running. A file to be processed by PGP generally contains text. This is the most common form of e-mail commu-

Table **3.**1

Summary of PGP Services

Function	Algorithms Used	Description
Digital signature	RSA, MD5	A hash code of a message is created using MD5. This message digest is encrypted using RSA with the sender's secret key, and included with the message.
Message encryption	IDEA, RSA	A message is encrypted using IDEA with a one-time session key generated by the sender. The session key is encrypted using RSA with the recipient's public key, and included with the message.
Compression	ZIP	A message may be compressed, for storage or transmission, using ZIP.
Email compatibility	Radix 64 conversion	To provide transparency for email applications, an encrypted message may be converted to an ASCII string using radix 64 conversion.
Segmentation	—	To accommodate maximum message size limitations, PGP performs segmentation and reassembly.

nication. But PGP can accept any type of file, including binary files, Postscript files, PICT files, and so on. One of the convenient services provided by PGP is that it enables the user to send files via e-mail that would ordinarily not be acceptable to the e-mail system.

In any case, the preparation of the file for PGP processing is outside the scope of PGP itself. A text file may be prepared by a word processor, a PICT file by a drawing program, and so forth. In short, the raw material for PGP, the file, is provided by the user.

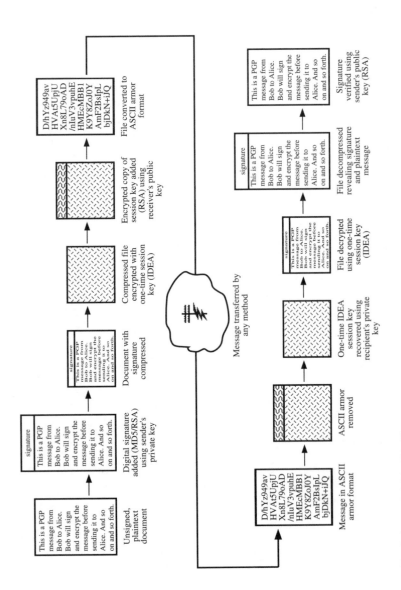

Fig **3.1**   PGP: The Big Picture

The Digital Signature

Given some file as input, the first potential step for PGP is the creation of a digital signature to attach to the file. This is an optional service. If the sender requests the digital signature, then PGP generates a hash code of the file using MD5 and then encrypts that hash code with RSA using the sender's private key. The resulting encrypted hash code is the digital signature for this file. The signature guarantees that this file is being sent by the user in question and that the file hasn't been altered after signing.

Compression

The next step, which is automatically performed unless the user explicitly disables the function, is compression. Most files, especially text files, contain a lot of redundancy, and it is possible to reduce the size of the file considerably without losing any information. PGP will take the file plus signature and compress them both to produce a compressed block of data.

Encryption

The next step, which is optional, is message encryption. This is the function that provides confidentiality. We want to encrypt the message in such a way that only the intended recipient can recover it. One approach is to use RSA and encrypt the entire message with the recipient's public key. Then, since only the recipient has the matching private key, only the recipient could decrypt the message. The problem with this approach, as was mentioned in Chapter 2, is that RSA is quite slow. It would take an enormous amount of time to encrypt a sizable message using RSA or any public-key scheme. Instead, PGP has been designed to use the IDEA conventional encryption algorithm. It is a secure and very efficient algorithm.

But this raises another problem. If Bob is going to send a message to Alice encrypted with IDEA, how do Bob and Alice arrange to share a secret IDEA key that no one else possesses? If Bob is going to correspond with many other PGP users, then Bob will have to arrange a unique shared secret key with each possible correspondent. Furthermore, that shared key must kept secret by both parties for as long as they will ever want to correspond. The solution to this problem is a perfect example of using the right tool for the job. The message to be encrypted is, potentially, quite long. So PGP uses a random-number generator to generate an IDEA key and then encrypts the message with that key (called a session key). Now, because IDEA is a conventional encryption algorithm, the session key has to be sent to the recipient as well. To protect the session key, it is RSA-encrypted with the recipient's public key and then attached to the IDEA-encrypted message. In this manner, only the recipient can recover the session key and use it to decrypt the message. IDEA is fast, so the message encryption is reasonably quick; although RSA is slow, the IDEA key is only 128 bits long, so the RSA encryption process isn't overly time-consuming. (Note that the session key is only used once, to encrypt this one message; PGP will generate a new IDEA key for the next message.)

Thus Bob doesn't need to worry about setting up a shared IDEA key with every potential correspondent. When Bob wants to communicate with Alice, or anyone else, all Bob has to do is obtain a copy of that person's public key.

E-Mail Compatibility

If signing, or compression, or encryption is performed on the original file, the block of data produced by PGP won't consist of readable text. Instead, the block will include arbitrary binary data. However, most e-mail systems cannot deal with arbitrary data but can only handle text files. To accommodate this restriction, PGP converts raw binary data into a stream of printable characters. The result is sometimes referred to as *ASCII armor*. ASCII stands for American Standard Code for Information Interchange. It is a standardized way of defining text characters with seven-bit codes. The result of the ASCII armor process is a string of characters, all of which are printable ASCII characters. The term armor refers to the fact that the character set used is such that the file will be able to make it through any e-mail system without alteration.

One interesting byproduct of the ASCII armor format is that even a plaintext message that is signed but not compressed or encrypted is unreadable by the casual human observer. Of course,

if the observer knows the message is in ASCII armor format, it is a
simple matter to recover the original message.
     If you do send an unencrypted plaintext file with a signature,
PGP offers the option of applying the ASCII armor only to the signature. This makes it possible for the recipient to read the message without bothering with PGP. In this case PGP is only needed
by the recipient to verify the signature.

Receiving a PGP Message

The bottom portion of Figure 3.1 shows the receipt of a PGP
message. Basically, at the receiving end, PGP simply reverses the
processing done at the sending end. First, the ASCII armor i'
removed by converting from the ASCII armor format back to th
binary format. Next, if the message is encrypted, PGP recovers the
session key. The session key was encrypted using RSA with the
recipient's public key, so PGP uses the recipient's private key to
decrypt it. With the session key in hand, PGP then decrypts the
message using the IDEA decryption algorithm. The next step is to
decompress the message. This simply reverses the compression
algorithm used at the sending end.
     Finally, if the message was signed, PGP verifies the signa-
ture. The signature was encrypted using the sender's private key,
so PGP uses the sender's public key to decrypt. This exposes the
hash code for this message. PGP does its own calculation of the
hash code and compares it with the one in the signature. If the two
match, the signature is verified.

Segmentation and Reassembly

One PGP function not illustrated in Figure 3.1 is segmentation and reassembly. E-mail facilities are often restricted to a maximum message length. For example, many of the facilities accessible through the Internet impose a maximum length of 50,000
bytes. Any message longer than this must be broken up into smaller segments, each of which is mailed separately.
     To accommodate this restriction, PGP automatically subdi-
vides a message that is too large into segments that are small
enough to send via e-mail. The segmentation is done after all of
the other processing, including the ASCII armor conversion. Thus,

the session key component and signature component appear only once, at the beginning of the first segment. At the receiving end, PGP must strip all the e-mail headers and reassemble the entire original block before performing the steps illustrated in the lower half of Figure 3.1.

Now let us examine each of the PGP functions more closely.

3.2 PGP IS NOT E-MAIL

After PGP has created a message, the entire PGP message is delimited by two boundaries. The beginning boundary is the string

```
-----BEGIN PGP MESSAGE-----
Version: x.x
```

Where x.x indicates the version number. The ending boundary is the string

```
-----END PGP MESSAGE-----
```

As an example, Figure 3.2 shows the contents of a text file. In this case, it happens to be that marvelous song about PGP by the filk (yes, *filk* not *folk*) singer and composer Leslie Fish. Figure 3.3 shows the result of passing this through PGP, including signing, compressing, message encrypting, and ASCII armor formatting.

But note that the result isn't an e-mail message: It is simply a text file. The beauty of this is that the text file can be sent using any e-mail system. The boundaries encapsulate the PGP message so that the entire message can be treated as the text portion of an e-mail message. The overall e-mail message will consist of the header used by the mail transport service and the body of the e-mail message, which is the encapsulated PGP message. Furthermore, this technique enables mail systems to assemble multiple messages in a single envelope without fear of disturbing the contents of the messages.

Figure 3.4 shows an e-mail message received by Alice from Bob containing the PGP file of Figure 3.3. In this case the message was sent from a Compuserve system to an Internet address.

```
                              P.G.P.

            (words & music by Leslie Fish (c)12/18/93)

    The G-men all are cryin' and tearin' out their hair,
    'Cause there's a new cryptography that's shown up everywhere.
    Nobody can break it, however good they be.
    Everybody's PC's got the PGP.


    It guarantees who's callin' and just who gets the call.
    If you ain't got your code-phrase, then you can't get in at all.
    Oh, there ain't nothin' like it to keep your privacy.
    Half the world's computers got the PGP.


    There's not a way to crack it, not in a hundred years.
    All the spooks and wiretappers are cryin' in their beers.
    They can't spy on citizens, here or oversea
    When every home computer's got the PGP.


    Bless the man who made it, and pray that he ain't dead.
    He could've made a million, if he'd sold it to the Feds,
    But he was hot for freedom; he gave it out for free.
    Now every common citizen's got PGP.


    So go say what you want to, of love or war or hate,
    Kinky sex, or dirty words, or overthrow the state.
    Nobody can stop you. Speech is really free
    When everybody's PC's got the PGP.
```

Fig **3.2**   Input to PGP

3.3 PUBLIC KEYS AND PRIVATE KEYS

Fundamental to the operation of PGP is the requirement that each user have a private key as well as a copy of the public key of each potential correspondent. This simple statement hides a rather sub-

```
-----BEGIN PGP MESSAGE-----
Version: 2.6

pgAAA11dN5DK8v6FXTVTRBNg1kG1ztpAU4o6Sia6qT7+/nzmV9wAK9yTiGGx3qRM
2tfzPkOtOsf2vyeaN2ZM+fAVJm1EFT1604xN93dHuC6mFL5yKYoCeRINfHSZvj8r
XMFnrffOMJWrSjYL0aZ4ts71W0c+icCCkUEHLj2aH/8hKCtEvq9oMTiKc0JwmWxC
4TyRMrQpLOb1G7aX12zBut26tujTjpA1yVs2Fei24u753oOZt4j5YSjVr7hUt81Q
I1IiRw+XytR3zxj3AhFBZYLyDr3WQw0f44SbnumarNXPQhNNn+0RgB654sPSvpZs
ilG7Ds1OHTtS9Y11CyZwbHX6Xm/sr4A6ZwOwlgFAj6r9b1Vn1VPR2u7tAd/Nw2oX
uEzye+s6ZJIPmla6LGiPtLKiTPM1cH2UVrvq0iRfX73J9x1qfMZOOwp4ezGdiX+m
9+aEbzukiuP845zHPhN/ugvtrL497mhyZx6qZ6BTprr2jZKDRmf3squmcyUr8f5Q
nnZXok/CagWrhn6Gj1yZ8b30onrZRP5hspPcuI3S3kYsp9j7ihpA3XFtV9koI430
jw/eb5SYv2S68gEoLUcxFDcSYiZHFGW/+JXB9409FAAwlnKIoiDaav98g5kYW+Bb
oz/1tqr0LvBPch0HA0ns2q0wmsZNsC5qBqOhDfV/02st/SuFBTXJqFi5Qf71cMAN
7oBc62bSssRnfkhxs5GY0402Bmchgaz6bQQEkTaN46syDhoDdMI4nfFBA5P1t145
a2ujvFyCezh+QScfOcSybSnJrRGaAzf12+zBQ43zqOYcrvds4aJM4vqoReiQjILe
zlbGuU80erFE9o34w/zATrE0JjwM/wE110XrT7PIN5GD5GqJKT0DyLhYtk2oIGem
nPsI/9m6qDXhtg6GP2wse56Q/CUKtyLRZaVyVvQUT0gFOnxqBRVRSniU9g/7Uq25
VIGUQnhtPeS/PRgxyxYgVKuDczfzJ/38ZMLhNMocFdO5bk65ZcvSzoI1BTDFYfoz
cf2gjRS1WX7kZvubLSmCGR1UcYgmWGt7GNINLPpsAsk2Su/47sDSiqZ9qH+iX9Cu
9DnBZW8oxKHwhu5gXeOHwj1NLUAWgK1ZtWoqxcpN2P8mQFt45Gr1sXYGVZ+9egfW
SW0=
=Z25G
-----END PGP MESSAGE-----
```

Fig **3.3**   Output from PGP

stantial complex of interrelated issues, and Chapters 5 and 6 are devoted to sorting out all of the issues. For this chapter, all we really need to know is the general scheme for maintaining these keys within PGP.

Public Keys

PGP maintains a list of public keys that the user has obtained by one means or another. These keys are collected and stored on a *public key ring*. Each item on the ring actually includes several parts:

```
From 12345.6789@compuserve.com Fri Jul  8 19:44:27 1994
Date: 08 Jul 94 15:53:10 EDT
From: Bob <12345.6789@compuserve.com>
To: Alice@system.net
Subject: Leslie's Song

-----BEGIN PGP MESSAGE-----
Version: 2.6

pgAAA11dN5DK8v6FXTVTRBNg1kG1ztpAU4o6Sia6qT7+/nzmV9wAK9yTiGGx3qRM
2tfzPkOtOsf2vyeaN2ZM+fAVJm1EFT1604xN93dHuC6mFL5yKYoCeRINfHSZvj8r
XMFnrffOMJWrSjYL0aZ4ts71W0c+icCCkUEHLj2aH/8hKCtEvq9oMTiKc0JwmWxC
4TyRMrQpLOb1G7aX12zBut26tujTjpA1yVs2Fei24u753oOZt4j5YSjVr7hUt81Q
I1IiRw+XytR3zxj3AhFBZYLyDr3WQw0f44SbnumarNXPQhNNn+0RgB654sPSvpZs
ilG7Dsl0HTtS9Y11CyZwbHX6Xm/sr4A6ZwOwlgFAj6r9blVnlVPR2u7tAd/Nw2oX
uEzye+s6ZJIPmla6LGiPtLKiTPM1cH2UVrvq0iRfX73J9x1qfMZOOwp4ezGdiX+m
9+aEbzukiuP845zHPhN/ugvtrL497mhyZx6qZ6BTprr2jZKDRmf3squmcyUr8f5Q
nnZXok/CagWrhn6Gj1yZ8b30onrZRP5hspPcuI3S3kYsp9j7ihpA3XFtV9koI430
jw/eb5SYv2S68gEoLUcxFDcSYiZHFGW/+JXB94O9FAAwlnKIoiDaav98g5kYW+Bb
oz/ltqr0LvBPch0HA0ns2q0wmsZNsC5qBqOhDfV/02st/SuFBTXJqFi5Qf71cMAN
7oBc62bSssRnfkhxs5GY04O2Bmchgaz6bQQEkTaN46syDhoDdMI4nffFBA5P1t145
a2ujvFyCezh+QScfOcSybSnJrRGaAzf12+zBQ43zqOYcrvds4aJM4vqoReiQjILe
zlbGuU80erFE9o34w/zATrE0JjwM/wE110XrT7PIN5GD5GqJKT0DyLhYtk2oIGem
nPsI/9m6qDXhtg6GP2wse56Q/CUKtyLRZaVyVvQUT0gFOnxqBRVRSniU9g/7Uq25
VIGUQnhtPeS/PRgxyxYgVKuDczfzJ/38ZMLhNMocFdO5bk65ZcvSzoI1BTDFYfoz
cf2gjRS1WX7kZvubLSmCGR1UcYgmWGt7GNINLPpsAsk2Su/47sDSiqZ9qH+iX9Cu
9DnBZW8oxKHwhu5gXeOHwj1NLUAWgK1ZtWoqxcpN2P8mQFt45Gr1sXYGVZ+9egfW
SW0=
=Z25G
-----END PGP MESSAGE-----
```

Fig **3.4**   E-Mail Message

1. The public key itself
2. The User ID of the owner of this public key; typically the owner's name
3. A Key ID, which is a unique identifier for this key

4. Other information related to the trustworthiness of the key and its owner

Let's not worry about that last point for now; we will study that in detail in Chapter 6. The significance of the User ID and the key ID is that they provide two different ways of grabbing a key from the ring. PGP can retrieve a person's key from the public key ring given that person's name or given the Key ID. We will see examples of both applications.

Private Keys

To use PGP, you must have a private key. It's acceptable to have several private keys; for example, you might want two different keys of different lengths. But you must have at least one private key.

So, the first thing you should do after installing PGP is generate a key pair. Recall that RSA produces a matching public-private key pair when generating keys. When the two keys are generated, PGP places the public key on your public key ring. As with other keys on that ring, it has a user ID (yours) and a key ID.

The other half of the pair, the private key, must be handled with more care. This key is to be stored on your *private key ring*. This ring stores your private key or keys and only your private keys. Obviously, your private key ring doesn't contain the private key of any other user. You don't know and don't need to know anyone else's private key. More importantly (to you), no one else should know your private key. Therefore PGP doesn't simply store your private key on the private key ring. Instead, PGP asks the user for a *passphrase*, which is any sequence of characters made up by the user. It is called a passphrase rather than a password since it need not be a single word. An example of a passphrase is T42andME4U. PGP then uses that passphrase to generate a 128-bit IDEA key[1] and encrypts the private key using IDEA and the passphrase-based key. PGP stores the private key on the private key ring and discards the passphrase and the IDEA key.

---

[1] The passphrase is input to the MD5 algorithm, which produces a 128-bit hash code. This hash code is used as the IDEA key.

TIP

Two rules for the passphrase that you select: (1) It should be easy to remember, so that you don't have to write it down, and (2) it should be hard to guess so that it is secure from attack. Some advice on this subject is found in Chapter 13.

The private key ring includes the following pieces of information for each private key:

1. The private key, encrypted using the passphrase-based IDEA key
2. The owner's User ID
3. The Key ID of the corresponding public key; which links the private key with its public key on the public key ring

Whenever you attempt to retrieve a private key from your private key ring, PGP will prompt you for the passphrase. After you correctly type in your passphrase, PGP will grab the private key from the ring and decrypt it, using IDEA, with the key generated from your passphrase. Once this copy of the private key is used, it is immediately discarded.

As a result of these precautions, even if someone steals your private key ring, it will do them no good without the passphrase. Remember the passphrase but don't write it down.

3.4 DIGITAL SIGNATURES

The digital signature scheme used by PGP is essentially the one discussed in Chapter 2 and illustrated in Figure 2.5. Figure 3.5 provides a close-up of the message-signing process. The sequence is:

1. The sender creates a message.
2. PGP uses MD5 to generate a 128-bit hash code of the message.
3. The sender specifies the private key to be used for this operation and provides a passphrase, enabling PGP to decrypt the sender's private key.
4. PGP encrypts the hash code with RSA using the sender's

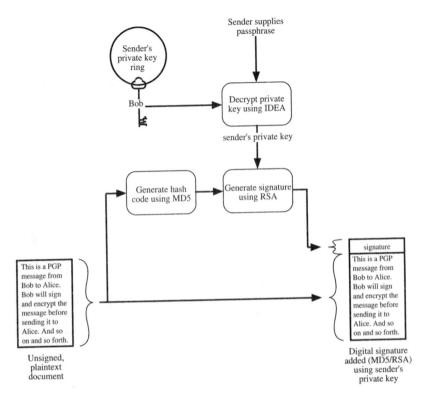

Fig **3.5** Signing a Message

private key, and attaches the result to the message. The key ID of the corresponding sender's public key is attached to the signature.

Now let's look at what happens on the receiving end (Figure 3.6):

1. PGP takes the key ID attached to the signature and uses that to grab the correct public key from the public key ring.
2. PGP uses RSA with the sender's public key to decrypt and recover the hash code.
3. PGP generates a new hash code for the message and compares it with the decrypted hash code. If the two match, the message is accepted as authentic.

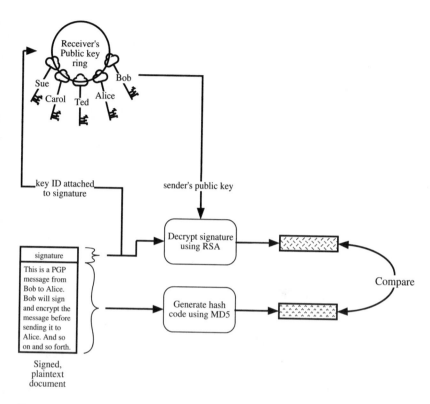

Fig **3.6**   Verifying the Signature on a Message

Note that Alice's public key ring contains a copy of her own public key. There is normally no operational use of this key by Alice. However, from time to time, Alice will want to provide her public key to others and her public key ring is a handy place to store it.

The combination of MD5 and RSA provides an effective digital signature scheme. Because of the strength of RSA, the recipient is assured that only the possessor of the matching private key can generate the signature. Because of the strength of MD5, the recipient is assured that no one else could generate a new message that matches the hash code and, hence, the signature of the original message.

3.5 COMPRESSION

As a default, PGP compresses the message after applying the signature but before encryption. This has the benefit of saving space both for e-mail transmission and for file storage.

PGP makes use of a compression package called ZIP, written by Jean-loup Gailly, Mark Adler, and Richard Wales. ZIP is a freeware package written in C that runs as a utility on UNIX and other systems. ZIP is functionally equivalent to PKZIP, a widely available shareware package developed by PKWARE, Inc. for MS-DOS systems. The zip algorithm is perhaps the most commonly used cross-platform compression technique; freeware and shareware versions are available for Macintosh and other systems as well as MS-DOS and UNIX systems.

In essence, the zip algorithm looks for repeating strings of characters in the input and replaces subsequent instances of such strings with compact codes. The destination system performs the same scanning function and is able to recognize the codes generated by the source and replaces these with the original text. The more redundancy there is in the input, the more effective the zip algorithm is in finding such sequences and the more heavily it can rely on codes. Typical text files compress to about one-half of their original length.

3.6 MESSAGE ENCRYPTION

Another basic service provided by PGP is confidentiality, which is provided by encrypting messages to be transmitted or stored locally as files. In both cases the conventional encryption algorithm IDEA is used. Recall that IDEA makes use of a 128-bit key.

As always, one must address the problem of key distribution. In PGP each conventional key is used only once; that is, a new key is generated as a random 128-bit number for each message. Thus, although this key is referred to in the documentation as a session key, it is in reality a one-time key. Because it is to be used only once, the session key is bound to the message and transmitted with it. To protect the key, it is RSA-encrypted with the receiver's public key. Figure 3.7 illustrates the sequence, which can be described as follows:

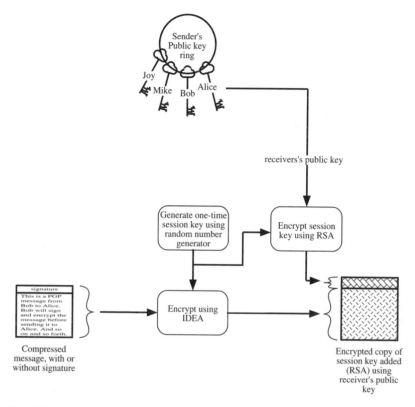

Fig **3.7**   Encrypting a Message

1. PGP generates a random 128-bit number to be used as a session key for this message only.
2. PGP encrypts the message, using IDEA with the session key.
3. PGP encrypts the session key with RSA, using the recipient's public key, and attaches the result to the message. The key ID of the recipient's public key is attached to the encrypted session key.

Note that Bob's public key ring (Figure 3.7) differs from Alice's (Figure 3.6). A user's public key ring contains the public keys that this user has collected. Each user is responsible for col-

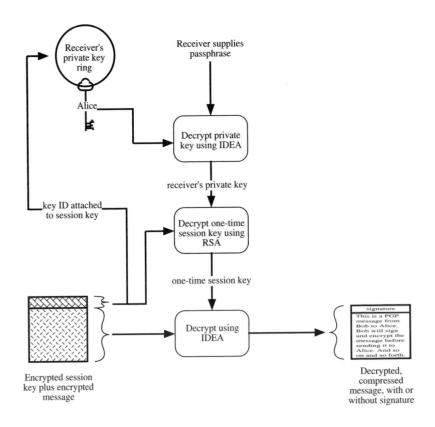

Fig **3.8**   Decrypting a Message

lecting the public keys that he or she needs, so it is unlikely that
two public key rings will have the same set of keys.

Turning to the receiving end (Figure 3.8):

1. PGP takes the key ID attached to the message and uses
   that to grab the correct private key from the private key
   ring. Recall that a user may have more than one private
   key.
2. The recipient provides a passphrase, enabling PGP to
   decrypt the recipient's private key.

3. PGP uses RSA with the private key to decrypt and recover the session key.
4. PGP decrypts the message using IDEA with the session key.

One can make several observations. First, to reduce encryption time the IDEA/RSA combination is used instead of just using RSA to directly encrypt the message; IDEA is substantially faster than RSA. Also, using RSA solves the session key distribution problem, because only the recipient is able to recover the session key that is bound to the message. Finally, the use of one-time conventional keys strengthens what is already a strong conventional encryption approach. Only a small amount of plaintext is encrypted with each key and there is no relationship among the keys.

As we have seen, both encryption services may be used for the same message. First, a signature is generated for the plaintext message and attached to the message. Then, after compression is used, the compressed plaintext message plus signature is encrypted using IDEA, and the session key is encrypted using RSA.

In summary, when both services are used, the sender first signs the message with his/her own private key, then encrypts the message with a session key, and then encrypts the session key with the recipient's public key.

3.7 E-MAIL COMPATIBILITY

When PGP is used, at least part of the block to be transmitted is encrypted. If only the signature service is used, then the message digest is encrypted (with the sender's private RSA key). If the confidentiality service is used, both the message and the signature (if present) are encrypted (with a one-time IDEA key). Thus, part or all of the resulting block consists of a stream of arbitrary eight-bit bytes. However, many electronic mail systems only permit the use of messages consisting of ASCII text. To accommodate this restriction, PGP provides the service of converting the raw data to a stream of printable ASCII characters. This conversion is done by mapping each group of three bytes of binary data into four ASCII characters; the format of the result is referred to as *ASCII armor*.

The use of ASCII armor expands a message by 33%. Fortunately, the session key and signature portions of the message are relatively compact and the plaintext message has been compressed. In fact, the compression should be more than enough to compensate for the ASCII armor expansion. We mentioned that ZIP produces a typical compression ratio of about 2 to 1. If we ignore the relatively small signature and key components, the typical overall effect of compression and expansion of a file of length X would be $1.33 \times 0.5 \times X = 0.665 \times X$. Thus, there is still an overall compression of about one-third.

One noteworthy aspect of the ASCII armor algorithm is that it blindly converts the input stream to ASCII armor format regardless of content, even if the input happens to be ASCII text. Thus, if a message is signed but not encrypted, and the conversion is applied to the entire block, the output will be unreadable to the casual observer, which provides a certain level of confidentiality. As an option, PGP can be configured to convert to ASCII armor format only the signature portion of signed plaintext messages. This enables the recipient to read the message without using PGP, although PGP would still have to be used to verify the signature.

3.8 THE ORDER OF OPERATIONS IN PGP

The order in which the five functions of digital signature, compression, message encryption, conversion to ASCII armor format, and segmentation are performed is critical. The signature is generated first, on the plaintext message, for two reasons:

1. It is preferable to sign a plaintext message so that one can store only the plaintext message together with the signature for future verification. If one signed a compressed or encrypted file, then it would be necessary either to store that version of the message for later verification or to recompress and/or re-encrypt the message when verification is required.

2. Even if one were willing to generate a recompressed message dynamically for verification, PGP's compression algorithm presents a difficulty. The algorithm isn't deterministic: Various implementations of the algorithm achieve different running speed versus compression ratio trade-offs, and as a result produce different compressed forms. How-

ever, these different compression algorithms are interoperable, because any version of the algorithm can correctly decompress the output of any other version. Applying the hash function and signature after compression would constrain all PGP implementations to exactly the same realization of the compression algorithm.

So the digital signature must come first, before compression or message encryption. The reason for performing message encryption after compression is to strengthen cryptographic security. The essence of a compression algorithm is to reduce redundancy in a block of message, which increases cryptographic security in two ways:

1. Some forms of cryptanalysis rely on exploiting regularities in the plaintext to determine the key which has generated a given ciphertext. Compression tends to eliminate those regularities.
2. When a brute-force attack is made, that is, when every possible key is tried, the attacker must examine each attempted decryption to determine success. If the plaintext is in compressed form, it may not be clear that a given decryption has yielded a valid plaintext. Of course, the attacker can perform a decompression on the result of each trial decryption, but this increases the cost of the brute-force attack.

Next, the ASCII armor conversion must be performed after digital signature, compression, and message encryption, so that the result is ready for transmittal over an e-mail facility. Finally, it is only after conversion to ASCII armor format that the final size of the message is attained, which is the appropriate time to apply segmentation.

CHAPTER 4

PGP Features

Chapter 3 summarized the basic services of PGP: digital signature, compression, message encryption, and e-mail compatibility. In this chapter, we look at some of the additional features of PGP that increase its usefulness.

4.1 MULTIPLE RECIPIENTS

Suppose you have a file that you wish to send to more than one person. You could create a PGP message for each recipient and send these in separate e-mail messages. However, PGP provides a more convenient and compact method in which a single message is created that can then be sent to multiple recipients: This feature illustrates one of the major strengths of public-key encryption, namely, its flexibility.

The technique is surprisingly simple. A user creates a file and instructs PGP to sign and encrypt it for multiple recipients. PGP signs the file using the sender's private key. Since all recipients will have the same public key for this recipient, only one copy of the signature need be attached to the file. Next, PGP compresses the file and then generates a random 128-bit IDEA key and encrypts the compressed file.

Now, recall that at this point, for a single recipient, PGP would encrypt the session key with the recipient's public key and attach that to the message, together with the key ID of the public key. For multiple recipients, PGP merely repeats this process for each recipient (Figure 4.1). PGP encrypts the *same IDEA key* once

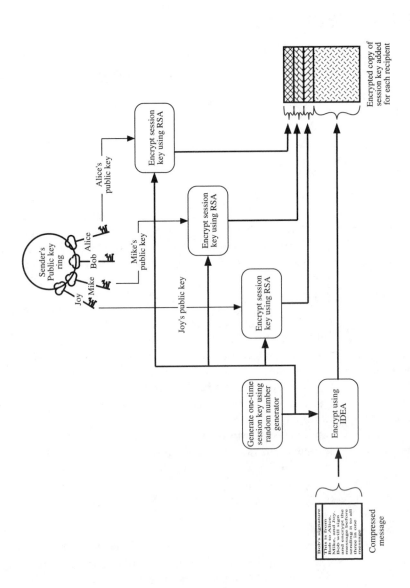

Fig **4.1**   Encrypting a Message for Multiple Recipients

for each recipient, using that recipient's public key. Each encrypted key, together with the corresponding public key ID, is attached
to the file. When the encrypted file is delivered, the recipient's
PGP scans the attached key IDs for one that matches a key ID on
its private ring, ignoring the others. It then proceeds as usual to
recover the IDEA key. PGP then strips off all of the encrypted
IDEA keys and finally decrypts the encrypted message. Since an
encrypted IDEA key, together with the public key ID, is quite
small, the presence of multiple encryptions of the session key on
the message adds little to its length.

The encrypted message can now be sent to each recipient. If
the sender's mail program supports aliases for multiple recipients
(virtually all do), then the sender would only have to address the
message once. The mail program would then take care of sending
an identical copy of the encrypted message to each recipient.

WARNING

The identities of the recipients is not completely hidden by PGP. If you
attempt to decrpyt a file and enter an incorrect passphrase, PGP will
print out a message listing those who can read this message. Each
entry in the list will either be a User ID (if this user's key is on your public key ring) or a Key ID (if this user's key is not on your public key ring).

4.2 ENCRYPTING LOCAL FILES

PGP provides the option of encrypting a file for local storage. In
this case, there is no need for public-key techniques, since only the
owner of the file will be performing the encryption and decryption.

The procedure is as follows (Figure 4.2):

1. The user supplies a filename and requests conventional
   encryption of the file.
2. PGP prompts the user for a one-time passphrase.
3. PGP uses the supplied passphrase to generate a conventional IDEA key.
4. PGP encrypts the file using IDEA with the key that has
   just been generated.

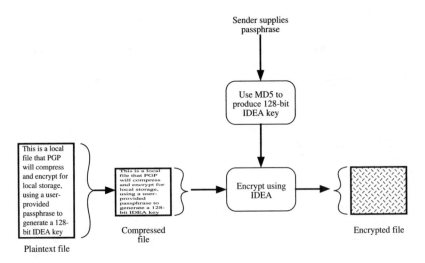

Fig **4.2**   Local File Encryption

When the user wishes to decrypt the file, PGP will prompt for the passphrase, generate the IDEA key, and decrypt the file.

This scheme is useful for storing archive files on either your system's hard disk or on backup disk or tape. In either case, if someone gains access to the encrypted files, they will be unable to recover the plaintext.

Note that you could achieve the same objective by encrypting a file with your public key. The method described in this section takes less time to execute.

TIP

The conventional encryption option is certainly useful for protecting files on diskettes and your hard disk at home, but it is also a useful travel tool. If you travel with a notebook system, then your files are much more vulnerable on that system than in your home. It is a good idea to encrypt all of the sensitive files on that system just before a trip. For convenience, you can use the same passphrase for all of the files.

You might be interested to know that if you encrypt the same file on two different occasions, using the same passphrase (and therefore the same IDEA key), PGP will produce two different ciphertext outputs. The reason for this is that PGP inserts a random 64-bit prefix at the beginning of the plaintext before encryption, which alters the ciphertext. Upon decryption, this prefix is revealed and discarded.

TIP

Don't use the same passphrase for encrypting local files that you use to encrypt your private key. Your private key is the foundation of your security in the use of PGP and the less often you use it, the less likely it will be compromised.

4.3 THE DISPLAY-ONLY OPTION

Normally, when a recipient processes an incoming PGP message, PGP decrypts the message and stores it in a file. Alternatively, the sender can direct that the plaintext be displayed only rather than stored by using what is known as the "for your eyes only" option.

When the sender exercises this option, the ciphertext will be marked internally to indicate that the option has been selected. On the receiving end, when the recipient attempts to decrypt and store the message, the plaintext will be displayed on the user's screen but is not saved to disk. According to Phil Zimmermann, "This feature was added at the request of a user who wanted to send intimate messages to his lover, but was afraid she might accidentally leave the decrypted message on her husband's computer."

When this option is used, PGP will display the message one screen at a time. After each screen is displayed, the user must hit the space bar to see the next screen; this is the same technique of the UNIX "more" command. To see the message again, the recipient must decrypt it again.

This option isn't foolproof and may be easily defeated. There are a variety of ways to capture a screen and save it to a file or redirect screen output to a file. This option isn't intended to be fail-safe. Rather, its purpose is to alert the recipient that this is a message that probably shouldn't be saved in plaintext form.

4.4 WIPING

As an option, you can have PGP delete a plaintext file after encrypting it. Typically, when a file is deleted by an operating system, only its entry in the file directory is erased and the corresponding disk space is released. However, the actual bits of the file remain on the disk until they are overwritten by another file write. It is because the file itself remains temporarily intact that it is often possible to recover deleted files with one of the many available file recovery utilities.

In the case of PGP, however, the deletion option ensures that the plaintext file cannot be recovered except by decryption of the corresponding ciphertext. Accordingly, PGP not only deletes the plaintext file but also performs a file-wiping operation; the plaintext file is overwritten before deletion. We can compare an ordinary file delete with putting sensitive documents in a wastepaper basket, and wiping with the use of a shredder.

Some versions of PGP overwrite with all zeros; others overwrite with random data. Keep in mind, however, that the PGP wipe feature only wipes the disk space occupied by the actual plaintext file. Word processors and editors typically make temporary copies of files. Once a file is saved and the program quits, these temporary files are deleted but, again, the actual disk blocks are untouched. If you are really concerned about leaving no traces of a plaintext file, use a utility that overwrites all unused blocks on a disk.

4.5 PROTECTING TEXT FILES

Electronic mail transport and delivery systems generally make the assumption that messages consist of printable characters only. Although these systems are designed to deliver a message that corresponds to the message that was originally submitted, liberties are sometimes taken. For example, the carriage-return, linefeed sequences delimiting lines in mail inbound to UNIX systems are transformed to single linefeeds as mail is written into local mailbox files. Similarly, on a Macintosh all lines end with just a carriage return and on DOS systems, lines terminate with a carriage return followed by a linefeed. Mail systems generally handle these conversions automatically. It is also possible that conversions between tabs and spaces may be performed in the course of mapping between the mail transmission format and a local format. These possibilities present two problems:

1. If a message is encrypted, the ciphertext may, by chance, contain one or more of the bit patterns that trigger processing, such as carriage-return, linefeed or a tab. Any modification to the ciphertext would prevent recovery of the plaintext by decryption.
2. If a message is encrypted, the transport and mail delivery systems cannot perform the end-of-line conversion, so that the text file that is the output of PGP at the receiving end won't be in the proper format.

PGP has a way to deal with both of these problems.

Protection from Alteration

The first of these problems is handled by ASCII armor formatting, described in Chapter 3. The result of the ASCII armor process is to convert all of the input into a stream of printable characters. The characters used are the upper- and lower-case letters, the digits 0 through 9, and the characters + and /. The carriage-return and linefeed characters aren't used in the conversion, nor is the tab or any other character that might be altered by the mail system. The result is a text file that is "immune" to the modifications inflicted by mail systems.

Another aspect of this problem is that some mail systems force the introduction of line terminations (a carriage return or a linefeed or both) when presented with a text file with very long lines. This isn't a problem for PGP since it will ignore these line-termination characters in converting back from ASCII armor format. However, to avoid this processing, and also to make it easy to print out ASCII armor files, PGP automatically breaks up its ASCII armor output into lines of 64 characters each. Again, when PGP processes an ASCII armor file, it ignores the line-termination characters.

Treating Source as Text

To solve the second problem PGP will, as an option, convert any text input into what is known as canonical form. In essence, the *canonical form* uses a carriage-return, linefeed combination to terminate lines. If PGP is told to treat a source file as text, it will convert the input to this canonical form before further processing. At the receiving end, after message decryption and signature verification, PGP converts the plaintext from canonical form to whatever text form is appropriate for the local system (e.g., UNIX, Macintosh).

4.6 SIGNATURE OPTIONS

PGP provides quite a bit of flexibility in the use of signatures. Three examples are clear signing, detached signatures and retained signatures.

Clear Signing

Suppose that you wish to send a message via e-mail or to a USENET group that need not be concealed but which you wish to sign to guarantee its authenticity. You would like for the recipient to see that the message has been signed, but to be able to read the message without bothering to invoke PGP.

PGP provides an option, the clearsig option, that satisfies this requirement. As an example, consider the text file shown in Figure 4.3(a). Suppose that the clearsig option is on and that you invoke PGP to process that file with the following options:

1. Treat source file as text.
2. Sign but do not encrypt the file.
3. Use ASCII armor formatting.

The result, shown in Figure 4.3(b), is that PGP calculates the signature, converts the signature to ASCII armor format, and appends that to the plaintext.

Now, if the clearsig option is off and the same PGP operation is invoked, the result will be the file shown in Figure 4.3(c). PGP calculates the signature and attaches it to the plaintext. Then the

```
This is a test message that demonstrates the difference between clear
signing and not-so-clear signing.
```

(a) contents of file tstmsg.txt

```
-----BEGIN PGP SIGNED MESSAGE-----

This is a test message that demonstrates the difference between clear
signing and not-so-clear signing.

-----BEGIN PGP SIGNATURE-----
Version: 2.6

iQCVAgUBLliu3/XgUw9qEhrRAQF5IgP+NQHmZ5hLEOeEbkW6tP2JhYA1g5vU81PM
oSx2DXW16FSFjw6U6musTqAtDfDhCeDXqO3+asowFZmk6ifHQJ+W5S38rjb5f5vt
cDVl+GzrUnyP397MpiQiKPvShzOg61w3dPKkml07zF8AyfVsM5H3d92KT4E3Xh+X
fsL79gnEPRM=
=eW6V
-----END PGP SIGNATURE-----
```

(b) result of signing with clear signing option

```
-----BEGIN PGP MESSAGE-----
Version: 2.6

owHrZJjKxMqoF7Gu5euDYP4sIamLjIzLHVgYNlTkl8/9Zr73krxKwdSFGqWf/5r/
+sn84vRDwdvXHyRwHZyg+vj9w9sHVt59rec54/6J70tst7uvv5jOceVp/+3rBTfL
lbKX5RydL/u59kvF60n16z+wbZfpFJyy9+WDA51r2a2Wz9okbDNp7+Wdizv8pjF3
sFVdq56Rf9VrVn2r6o7vp4xFVjxas6BE3zcxOTOvJL84Q8HDBcQJcA8w0jNTcMvP
SUkt0ncqTUsDUiXFJbnF6XolFSUMQBCSkVmsAESJCiWpxSUKuanFxYnpqQolGYkl
Cimpufl5xSVFiUApoEiqQkomyITUvORUhaTUkvLU1DyF5JzUxCIFXXq7izPS8zLx0
hcS8FIW8/BLd4nxdiBRUQo+XCwA=
=Ks1Z
-----END PGP MESSAGE-----
```

(c) result of signing without clear signing option

Fig 4.3   Illustration of Clear Signing

entire result is converted to ASCII armor format. The output is
unreadable unless you have an implementation of PGP.

Note that PGP will only invoke clearsigning if the clearsig
option is set and all three of the command options listed above are
specified. In particular, if you do not specify "treat source file as

text" or you do not specify "use ASCII armor formatting," PGP will
not use the clear signing option.

Detached Signatures

Normally a signature is attached to the file that it signs. If
PGP processes a message in the usual fashion, it verifies the signature and then produces as output only the decrypted message;
the user doesn't have direct access to the signature. Since one normally wishes to verify a signature at the time of message recep-
tion, it is handy to have the signature attached to the message.

PGP also supports detached signatures. A detached signature
is a file that may be stored and transmitted separately from the
file it signs. This is useful in several contexts. Here are some
examples:

1. A user may wish to maintain a separate signature log of all
   messages sent or received.
2. A detached signature can be created for an executable program. Two possible uses of such a signature: First, the
   author of a program such as PGP can sign it, guaranteeing
   its authenticity; second, a signature can be used for virus
   detection. If a program is altered by a virus, then the signature will detect that; recall that once a file is signed, any
   modification to the file is detected during signature verification.
3. Detached signatures are also useful if more than one person is to sign a file. Each person signs the file separately
   and all of the signatures can be sent as a package along
   with the file. Otherwise, you would end up with "nested
   signatures," where each person signs the message plus all
   previous signatures.

Retained Signatures

PGP enables you to specify that the signature of a message be
retained after decryption and decompression, so that you are left
with a signed plaintext message. This is useful if you want to later
verify to yourself or anyone else that the message is authentic. For
example, Alice might receive a signed message from Marge. She

can forward this message to Ted, leaving Marge's signature intact and encrypting the message and the signature with PGP, using Ted's public key.

An important point: a file with a retained signature does not appear as a clear signed document. A retained signature is in binary format whereas the signature of a clear signed file is in ASCII armor format.

5

Key Generation and Secret Key Management

$\mathbf{T}$he starting point in your use of PGP is to create a public/secret key pair.[1] PGP does all the work but you do have some choices to make, including key size and User ID. We begin this chapter with an explanation of the issues involved in key generation and the choices to be made.

Once you have a public/secret key pair, it is vital that the secret key remain just that, secret. The remainder of this chapter is devoted to various aspects of protecting and managing secret keys.

5.1 CREATING PUBLIC/SECRET KEY PAIRS

Your first task when using PGP is to create an interrelated pair of keys, one public and one secret. This involves a dialog between you and PGP.

Public and Secret Keys

PGP uses the RSA public-key encryption algorithm, which was described briefly in Chapter 2. For those who are interested, Chapter 12 provides some mathematical details. However, only a minimal understanding of the ingredients of RSA keys is required for you to generate them. The two keys are made up of sets of related integers, the details of which are laid out in Table 5.1.

---

[1] All of the literature on public-key cryptography refers to public and private keys. However, since the PGP documentation, messages, and file names use *secret* in preference to *private*, we will follow that convention.

Table **5.1**

The Ingredients of RSA

Name	Symbol	Definition
modulus	n	The product of two prime numbers, p and q, selected at random.
public exponent	e	An integer whose value is constrained by the values of p and q.
private exponent	d	An integer whose value is determined by the values of e, p, and q.
public key	{e, n}	These two integers constitute the public key.
private key	{d, n}	Only d is secret, but both d and n are required to perform the operations expected of the secret key.

PRIME NUMBERS AND RSA

Prime numbers play an important role in the RSA algorithm. An integer is a prime number if and only if the only positive integers that divide it exactly are itself and 1. Thus, 5 is a prime number since its only exact divisors are 1 and 5, but 6 is not since it can be exactly divided by 1, 2, 3, and 6. It is difficult to determine whether a very large odd number is prime or not. An even harder problem is this: if a large number is the product of two primes, then determine those two prime numbers. The difficulty of this factorization problem is what makes the RSA algorithm so secure.

The RSA algorithm for generating a public/secret key pair is as follows:

1. RSA generates two random prime numbers p and q. The product of these two numbers, $n = p \times q$, is an element of both the public and secret keys.
2. The algorithm selects an integer e that satisfies certain constraints with respect to p and q.
3. A unique integer d is calculated from p, q, and e.

Given any plaintext as input, RSA can produce ciphertext as

output using the public key consisting of the integers e and n. This ciphertext can then be decrypted using the secret key consisting of d and n. Similarly, if the secret key $\{d, n\}$ is used to encrypt, then the public key $\{e, n\}$ can be used to decrypt.

The Key Generation Process

PGP key generation begins when the user requests that a new secret/public key pair be generated. The key generation process consists of the following steps.

1. PGP prompts the user for a passphrase to be used to encrypt the secret key.
2. PGP prompts the user to select a key size.
3. PGP asks for a User ID.
4. PGP asks the user to enter some keystrokes to assist in random number generation. Start typing at your normal pace, and PGP will indicate when you should stop, with the message "Enough, thank you."
5. PGP generates the two keys and places them on the public and secret key rings. While PGP is generating the keys, a series of periods and plus signs appear at the bottom of your screen; their purpose is to indicate that the generator is running.

Let's walk through this process step by step.

Passphrase   Secret keys are stored in encrypted form only. Otherwise, if someone managed to steal or copy your secret key ring, they could send messages in your name and decrypt messages sent to you. Since secret keys are always stored in encrypted form, an attacker has to obtain both your secret key ring and your passphrase to break the system.

Thus, an important element in the security of your secret key is the passphrase you select. We have a lot to say about this in Chapter 13, which you are encouraged to consult. For now, keep in mind these important rules:

Rule Number 1: *Select a passphrase that isn't easily guessed.*

This rule is not as easy to follow as you might think. Consider that if some one manages to get a copy your secret key ring, they can attack your secret key at leisure over an extended period of time, trying thousands or even millions of passphrases. So don't use: your name; your spouse or partner's name; names of well-known persons, fictional or real; any word in the spelling dictionary on your system; product names; titles of novels, plays, movies, TV programs; easily-recognized initials, such as TGIF or RTFM; any short combination of characters, say 7 or less; and on and on. A determined attacker will try words and phrases in all of the above categories, plus variations such as reversing the sequence of characters or capitalizing the first or last or all of the letters.

Rule Number 2: *Select a passphrase that you can remember.*

If you forget your passphrase there is no way to recover your secret key, no way. If your passphrase is a really tough one that would be impossible to guess but difficult to remember, such as `';lkjas0974uybldvc0-ew6rfh5lrfd-]08tyrhikj4e`, then you will be tempted to write it down, and the risk of compromise is obvious. So you must pick a passphrase that you can remember but that isn't easily guessed. See Chapter 13 for some guidance.

AVOID THIS MISTAKE

A mistake that some people make is to mumble their passwords, especially in their efforts to remember them. This is a critical mistake. So, if you think while you are typing, make sure your mouth isn't doing the thinking!

Rule Number 3: *The passphrase should be relatively easy to type.*

It is possible to store your passphrase in an environmental variable, PASSPHRASE, from your operating system's command shell. PGP can then retrieve your passphrase from this variable rather than prompting you for it. If your passphrase is very long or involves a number of case shifts, then typing it every time it is needed becomes a hassle and you will be tempted to store your passphrase. Even if you have a standalone system in your home, don't succumb to this temptation.

Rule Number 4: *Select a unique passphrase.*

Do not, repeat not, use any password or passphrase that you are using for any other purpose including your password to a shared UNIX system (this is a really bad mistake), your PIN, or any other password.

Rule Number 5: *Make sure you follow Rule Number 1.*

Key Size   The security of RSA depends on keeping d secret, which in turn depends on keeping p and q secret. However, since n is not secret, if an opponent can determine its two unique prime factors, then the scheme is broken. The larger the value of n, the more difficult the task. For very large values of n, it is effectively impossible to determine p and q, and therefore the secret key $\{d, n\}$ is secure.

When people refer to the key size of RSA, they are referring to the size of n, which determines the difficulty of breaking RSA. Unlike the case with IDEA and most other conventional encryption algorithms, the key size for RSA is variable; RSA will work with any size of n.

The tradeoff between security and speed is straightforward. The larger the value of n, the more secure the algorithm. However, the larger the value of n, the slower the encryption and decryption processes. We therefore need to strike a balance between security and speed.

No one can say with confidence exactly how big the RSA key must be to guarantee security. Techniques for determining the factors of prime numbers are constantly being refined and computational speeds continue to rise. It is best, therefore, to err on the side of caution.

In PGP the key size is a user option. Three standard options are offered:

- Casual (384 bits): known to be breakable, but with much effort
- Commercial (512 bits): possibly breakable by three-letter organizations
- Military (1024 bits): generally believed unbreakable

Most implementations of PGP also allow the user to pick any key size in the range of 384 to 1024 and some permit even larger keys sizes.

The choice of RSA key size is vital. IDEA, with its 128-bit conventional key, is universally recognized to be unbreakable with foreseeable technology using a brute-force key search. Although there is the possibility of some weakness in the IDEA algorithm itself, none has yet been disclosed and it seems, at least for now, unlikely. So, potentially, the weakest link in PGP is RSA.

HOW MANY PRIME NUMBERS ARE THERE?

When you select a key size of 1024 bits, PGP will generate at random two prime numbers of approximately 512 bits each, so that their product is a 1024-bit number. It should reassure you to know that there are roughly 3×10^{152} 512-bit prime numbers, which makes the attack on RSA for large key sizes very difficult.

There is one benchmark to help guide our decision of key size. To demonstrate RSA's strength, its three developers issued a challenge in August 1977 to decrypt a message that was encrypted using a 129-decimal-digit number (about 429 bits) as their public modulus. The authors predicted that it would take 40 quadrillion years with current technology to crack the code. In April 1994, the code was cracked after only eight months of work by a worldwide team cooperating over the Internet and using over 1600 computers.[2] This result doesn't invalidate the use of RSA; it simply means that larger key sizes must be used.

Based on the results of the so-called RSA-129 challenge, a key size of 384 bits can no longer be considered secure. A 512-key bit is still probably beyond the reach of all but the most determined efforts at cracking, but it makes no sense to stop there in your choice. Based on all available evidence, a 1024-bit key is far beyond the capabilities of the best-financed, best-equipped organizations to break and will remain so far into the future (maybe not 40 quadrillion years . . .). Since PGP only uses RSA to

---

[2] See the July 1994 issue of Scientific American for an account of this feat.

encrypt and decrypt the relatively short session keys and hash codes, the 1024-bit key doesn't present an undue computational burden. The only noticeable difference between a key size of 512 bits and one of 1024 bits is the amount of time needed to generate a key. Key generation time depends on the speed of your processor. Generation of a 1024-bit key will take from a few tens of seconds to a few minutes longer than generation of a 512-bit key. But, remember, you only have to generate the key once.

Finally, what about using an even larger key size, such as 2048 bits? The problem is that key sizes larger than 1024 bits aren't compatible with some PGP implementations. Since 1024 bits provides a level of security that satisfies all requirements, choose 1024 bits, and only 1024 bits, as your key size.

WHY SO BIG?

IDEA uses a key size of 128 bits and is considered extremely secure, yet a 128-bit key size for RSA poses little challenge to an attacker. Why must RSA keys be so big to achieve a comparable security level to that of IDEA? It has to do with the nature of the algorithms. In the case of IDEA, there is no known practical attack on the algorithm itself. The most promising course of attack on IDEA is the brute-force method of trying each possible key. In the case of RSA, an attack can be mounted on the algorithm itself. The attack is simply to find the two prime factors of an integer. For a 128-bit integer, the task of finding the two prime factors is relatively easy. For a 1024-bit integer, it is, for all practical purposes, impossible to find the two prime factors.

The choice of a key size for RSA is a well-known aspect of PGP. When PGP generates a key, it will ask you to select a key size. Less well-known is that the size of the public exponent, e, is also selectable. As a default, DOS PGP implementations use a value of e that is 5 bits in length and Macintosh PGP implementations use a value that is 17 bits in length. This relatively short length makes operations with public keys somewhat more efficient than those with secret keys. Thus, with a short bit length for e, encrypting session keys and checking signatures are more efficient operations than decrypting session keys and generating signatures.

But these differences in efficiency are of minor impact. The issue of concern is security. By and large, it is assumed that the use of a short bit length for e doesn't ease the task of breaking RSA. However, some experts in the field feel that the RSA's security is increased if the size of e is increased, up to a certain limit. If this very slight security risk is of concern to you, I suggest a bit length of 128 bits for e.

Your User ID   Your User ID should be something that clearly and uniquely identifies you. Typically, users employ a combination of their full name and their e-mail address in angle brackets, like so:

```
Robert Person <RPerson@company.com>
```

You may, however, be known by more than one name or have more than one e-mail address. In these cases, you might want to associate multiple User ID's with your key. For example, Bob may add the following User ID to his key:

```
Bob Person <BobP@university.edu>
```

Random Number Generation   Suppose that you have selected a key size of 1024 bits. PGP must then generate two prime numbers of 512 bits each. The technique used by PGP is to generate a series of 512-bit random numbers and test each to determine whether or not it is prime. The algorithm completes when it has found two prime numbers.

In fact, virtually all computer programs, including PGP, make use of what are known as *pseudorandom numbers* rather than true random numbers. A sequence of pseudorandom numbers is generated by some software algorithm. Hence, to some extent, the numbers generated are predictable. If the pseudorandom number stream generated by PGP were entirely predictable, then it would be possible for an opponent to guess the values of the two prime numbers chosen by PGP. To overcome this problem, PGP takes steps to make the psuedorandom number sequence as unpredictable as possible.

PGP's pseudorandom numbers are based on keystroke input from the user. Both the keystroke timing and the actual keys struck are used to generate the randomized stream. Thus, if the user hits arbitrary keys at a normal pace, a reasonably "random" input will be generated.

Key Storage Once PGP has completed the key generation process, it stores the secret key on the user's secret key ring and the public key on the user's public key ring. Recall that the secret key is encrypted using IDEA with a key derived from the user's passphrase.

Key Rings

The default keyrings that are used are the files `secring.pgp` and `pubring.pgp`. for the secret and public keyrings respectively. These files are stored in the same directory as the executable PGP program. Unless otherwise directed, PGP will use these key rings for the following actions:

- *Key generation:* When PGP generates a new key pair, it places the new secret key in `secring.pgp` and the corresponding public key in `pubring.pgp`. In fact, the entry in the secret key ring includes both the public and secret keys.
- *Signing:* PGP uses the first key in `secring.pgp` by default.
- *Decrypting a session key:* PGP uses the key in `secring.pgp` that matches the Key ID that is tied to the session key (see Chapter 3 for a discussion of session keys).
- *Verifying a signature:* PGP uses the key in `pubring.pgp` that matches the Key ID tied to the signature.
- *Key ring maintenance:* For any PGP command that involves adding, removing, or selecting a key, PGP uses `pubring.pgp`.

As an example, Figure 5.1 shows a display of the secret key ring of user Bob Person. The display includes the following elements:

- Type: `sec` for secret; `pub` for public key
- bits: the number of bits in the key

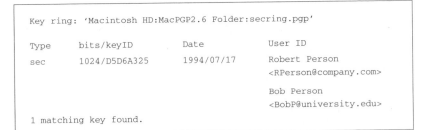

```
Key ring: 'Macintosh HD:MacPGP2.6 Folder:secring.pgp'

Type        bits/keyID         Date            User ID
sec         1024/D5D6A325      1994/07/17      Robert Person
                                               <RPerson@company.com>

                                               Bob Person
                                               <BobP@university.edu>

1 matching key found.
```

Fig **5.1**   Bob's Secret Key Ring

- keyID: the hexadecimal value of the rightmost 32 bits of the key ID for this key.
- date: the date this public/secret key pair was generated
- User ID: identifier of key owner

The actual key ID is the rightmost 64 bits of the key. However, for all practical purposes, a 32-bit key ID is likely to be unique within a single user's public or secret key ring. For the user's convenience, only the 32-bit key ID is displayed.

Figure 5.1 shows that Bob has one secret key with two User IDs.

Figure 5.2 displays Bob's public key ring. Most of the keys shown here were obtained by Bob from a file that accompanied the PGP package (in this case, MacPGP 2.6). The ring also includes the key for ViaCrypt, the distributor of a commercial version of PGP, and SLED, a public-key directory service (described in Chapter 15). Finally, of course, Bob's own public key is on this ring.

Note that the key ID for Bob's public key is the same as that for his secret key. The key ID is derived from the public key and is used to reference both the public and secret keys; this is the way that Bob's two keys are tied together.

TIP: PUTTING IMPORTANT KEYS FIRST

When PGP needs to access a key from the public key ring, it does a linear search from the beginning of the ring, looking for a match on User ID or Key ID, depending on the search. For a very large key ring, this search can take a long time. One solution is to have two public key

```
Key ring: 'Macintosh HD:MacPGP2.6 Folder:pubring.pgp'

Type     bits/keyID      Date          User ID
pub      1024/5F63A5B9   1994/02/08    Stable Large Email
                                       Database <sled@drebes.com>
pub      1024/CB768501   1993/10/13    ViaCrypt
                                       <Phone (602) 944-0773>

                                       ViaCrypt
                                       <70304.41@compuserve.com>

                                       ViaCrypt
                                       <viacrypt@acm.org>

                                       ViaCrypt
                                       <FAX (602) 943-2601>
pub      512/4D0C4EE1    1992/09/10    Jeffrey I. Schiller
                                       <jis@mit.edu>
pub      1024/0778338D   1993/09/17    Philip L. Dubois
                                       <dubois@csn.org>
pub      1024/FBBB8AB1   1994/05/07    Colin Plumb
                                       <colin@nyx.cs.du.edu>
pub      1024/C7A966DD   1993/05/21    Philip R. Zimmermann
                                       <prz@acm.org>
pub      709/C1B06AF1    1992/09/25    Derek Atkins
                                       <warlord@MIT.EDU>
pub      1024/8DE722D9   1992/07/22    Branko Lankester
                                       <branko@hacktic.nl>
pub      1024/9D997D47   1992/08/02    Peter Gutmann
                                       <pgut1@cs.aukuni.ac.nz>
pub      510/DC620423    1992/08/27    Jean-loup Gailly
                                       <jloup@chorus.fr>
pub      1024/28748E05   1992/09/06    Hugh A.J. Kennedy
                                       <70042.710@compuserve.com>
pub      1024/D5D6A325   1994/07/17    Bob Person
                                       <BobP@university.edu>

                                       Robert Person
                                       <RPerson@company.com>

12 matching keys found.
```

Fig 5.2   Bob's Public Key Ring

rings: one that is small and contains the most frequently-used keys, called `pubring.pgp`; and a larger key ring called something like `2ndring.pgp`. By default, PGP will search `pubring.pgp` unless you specify the other ring. The other solution is to reorganize your public ring to put frequently-used keys near the beginning. Each time a key is added to the ring it is put at the beginning. Therefore, to move a key to the beginning, extract that key from the ring, store it in a text file, and then add it back to the ring.

Backup Key Rings   PGP uses the term *backup key ring* in two different ways, which can lead to confusion. PGP maintains backup key rings for the default public and secret key rings, with file names `pubring.bak` and `secring.bak`, respectively. When PGP receives a command that requires modification of the default public key ring, PGP first replaces `pubring.bak` with a copy of the public key ring and then performs the modification on the public key ring. Therefore, PGP always maintains the current public key ring and a copy of that ring before the last change. Similarly, PGP maintains the current secret key ring and a copy of that ring before the last change.

PGP also allows the user to designate a backup copy of the user's secret key ring on some tamper-resistant medium, such as a write-protected diskette. PGP can be instructed to compare your public key on your current public key ring against the backup copy of the secret ring. Recall that each entry in a secret key ring actually includes both the public and the secret key information. Therefore, PGP can verify that the public key on your the public key ring matches the one saved on the write-protected backup secret key ring. This check assures the user that no one has tampered with the public key ring.

Selecting a Key   A number of PGP commands involve the selection of one or more keys from the secret or public key ring, such as viewing a key or removing a key from a ring. In an implementation that provides a graphical user interface (GUI), such as MacPGP, this selection is typically done by simply pointing and clicking. In an implementation based on a command-line interface, the user must specify the key or keys to be selected. There are two methods for doing this:

- Specify the full User ID or any fragment of the User ID. For example, if Bob enters *Derek* as a User ID, the key for Derek Atkins is returned (see Figure 5.2). If Bob enters *Philip* as a user ID, PGP will list the keys for both Philip Zimmermann and Philip L. Dubois.
- Specify the full Key ID or any fragment of the Key ID, preceded by "0x" to indicate a hexadecimal number. Thus, if Bob enters *0x63A5* as a Key ID, the SLED key is returned.

Selection by Key ID is useful when a ring contains more than one key from the same person, with the same User ID.

When a User ID or Key ID is entered, and more than one key matches, PGP will display the list of all such keys, followed by a line "*n* matching keys found", where *n* represents the number of keys found. If you simply ask for a display of all the keys on the ring, the matching string is in effect null and the ending statement indicates the total number of keys on the keyring. For example, Figure 5.2 ends with a line that indicates there are 12 keys on the key ring.

5.2 SECRET KEY MANAGEMENT

With respect to your secret key, you need to remember two things: First, you must protect your secret key so that it is virtually impossible for anyone else to obtain a copy and second, don't lose it!

Secret Key Protection

Location of Secret Ring   Ideally, confine the storage of your secret key to systems that you physically control. A computer that you use at home is fine. If you use a PC at work, it is best to store your secret key ring only on a write-protected diskette that you keep with you and not on the PC's hard disk.

What about a shared system, such as a shared UNIX system? There are two problems here. First, since your secret key ring is on the shared system, someone may be able to gain access to it and then attack the ring in an attempt to guess your passphrase. If you follow the guidelines of Chapter 13 for password selection and the five rules listed in Section 5.1, this risk is slight.

The second, much more serious risk is that you must communicate your passphrase to the shared system to use PGP. Thus your passphrase is transmitted over some kind of communications link, be it a LAN, a dedicated line, or a phone line if you are dialing in with a modem. In all of these cases, you have lost physical control of your passphrase. Now the security of your message depends on whichever is less secure: PGP or the line to the shared system.

Changing Your Passphrase   If you have reason to believe that your passphrase has been compromised but you are sure that no one has yet gained access to any of the copies of your secret key (there should only be one or two of these), then all is not lost. If you can change your passphrase before anyone has a chance to get at your secret key, security is maintained.

It is a simple matter to change your passphrase. PGP will prompt you for the current passphrase. This enables PGP to decrypt your secret key and also assures PGP that since you know the passphrase, you are authorized to change it. Then PGP prompts you for the new passphrase. PGP then encrypts your secret key, replaces the old secret key on your secret key ring, and discards the passphrase.

How Often Should I Change My Passphrase?

There are two schools of thought. One school holds that, sooner or later, you will accidentally reveal your passphrase. If you are in a public setting such as an office, someone may overhear you mumble the phrase as you enter it or look over your shoulder. A determined attacker may be able to use sophisticated electronic-intelligence techniques to monitor your home use and capture your passphrase as you enter it. Thus, to be safe, you should change the passphrase periodically so that if your passphrase is captured, the window of vulnerability of your secret key ring is small. The other school of thought is that the more often you change your passphrase, the more likely you are to forget the most recent one. If you are certain in your own mind that your passphrase is secure, then there is no good reason to change it.

Preserving Your Secret Key

In Chapter 6 we talk about the various ways to distribute

```
-----BEGIN PGP MESSAGE-----
Version: 2.6

lQHiAi4pFRsAAAEEAKgix5G3Ovg3hrI/vcMO5B5/jJRQQTb4AbYrwsbPtLY33NnG
TWx6XyvlYgoxxMbBEJXxPEa+5A5nfJkU0KsyBjhdsFfR5DWLllt5u529kxmUPw6m
XaDe/8j9iyIZv+x8jmbDE/uYsmd570AxfdoYpZrotaxkcbpoag/8z+rV1qMlABEB
AAEBnUxPfGULXMkD/ertre9FDD7DyyAKn8QLvtMx5JKueDhE1xEQpDi0aktQ9cB4
frKjQ6SCQE7J23ac0DYGbc/+olVKkzYdCjvMyucdOG1gssBfKbwUwgf7j5HoEBkD
jruoraVZJFFo001e0cfLpYgLH+cS4qbvmYNDkCEuu2Ibt2xhgyR3CcN0wzpmAgDA
GIhJU2zr/Xj81GkD1r0OmOpkIiqVA+IurvUr2Ctar4eHP8nJdIoiNyaHEH0eHp1i
4LEu62J+B1gNsGVfGKmdAgC2qtrgWolqvhSc3xM9T/nOl2vqrQ/x6pD+ta+RBJdt
vRf6Ti26v6meNdA3qO01o/P4ISlt2H2pNdyV3FlPIxEaAf9hZMET9BQeGPzvB799
9S/9GcZ6xA7RpYeTWnBoltBEy/VHoeWiyAKcCNj3o2OTVplrUWGIWd2fCbIfSY5m
Bj6Boa60JFJvYmVydCBQZXJzZb24gPFJQZXJzb25AY29tcGFnY29tcGFueT4=
IFB1cnNvbviA8Qm9iUEB1bm12ZXJzaXR5LmVkdT4=
=w6YH
-----END PGP MESSAGE-----
```

Fig 5.3   Bob's Secret Key

your public key in a trustworthy manner. Having gone to the trouble of distributing your public key, it is a major nuisance to lose your secret key. You then have to make sure that all potential correspondents (1) know that the old public key is obsolete and (2) get a copy of the new public key. To avoid these problems, take steps to preserve your secret key. The best way to do this is to copy your secret key ring to a diskette. If the ring on your system is ever corrupted, you can restore it from the diskette.

As an additional precaution, store an ASCII-armored hard copy of your secret key with the backup diskette. For example, Figure 5.3 shows Bob's secret key. This file is generated by telling PGP to extract a key from your secret key ring and to use ASCII armor. If necessary, you can then later (1) type this back in (very carefully!), (2) store it in a text file, and (3) add the key in the file to your secret key ring from the text file. It is important to realize that the ASCII-armored secret key shown in Figure 5.3 is password protected: This block doesn't contain the actual secret key but that key encrypted with IDEA using your passphrase as the IDEA key.

```
-----BEGIN PGP PUBLIC KEY BLOCK-----
Version: 2.6

mQCPAi4pFRsAAAEEAKgix5G3Ovg3hrI/vcMO5B5/jJRQQTb4AbYrwsbPtLY33NnG
TWx6XyvlYgoxxMbBEJXxPEa+5A5nfJkU0KsyBjhdsFfR5DWLllt5u529kxmUPw6m
XaDe/8j9iyIZv+x8jmbDE/uYsmd570AxfdoYpZrotaxkcbpoag/8z+rV1qM1ABEB
AAG0IEJvYiBQZXJzb24gPEJvYlBAdW5pdmVyc2l0eS51ZHU+tCRSb2J1cnQgUGVy
c29uIDxSUGVyc29uQGNvbXBhbnkubmFtZT4=
=43p4
-----END PGP PUBLIC KEY BLOCK-----
```

Fig **5.4**   Bob's Public Key

You can do the same thing with your public key, as shown in Figure 5.4. Again, with a hard-copy, ASCII-armor version of the public key, all that you need to do is type the text back into a text file and add the key to your public key ring.

Note that PGP explicitly indicates that the text file of Figure 5.4 contains a public key. This facilitates public key exchange, as we will see in Chapter 6. The text file of the secret key is not denoted as such, in line with the need to keep the secret key secure.

Moving Your Secret Key

Suppose you begin using PGP on a DOS system and generate a public/secret key pair. Over time, you distribute your public key to a number of people. Now you find that you want to also use PGP on a Macintosh system. Must you create a new public/secret key pair and alert all your correspondents?

The answer is no. We have just seen that it is possible to store your secret key in an ASCII-armored text file. You can load that file onto the other system and instruct PGP to add it to your secret key ring. The only technical problem is the compatibility between systems for reading and writing text files. There are a number of utilities that allow you to transfer text files between different platforms, such as DOS and Macintosh, via diskette.

Another possibility, if both systems have access to the Internet, is to mail the secret key from one system to the other. In this case, encrypt the ASCII-armored file containing your secret key using the local file encryption technique described in Chapter 4, with a one-time passphrase. Once the file is on the target system, you can decrypt it with the one-time passphrase, revealing the ASCII-armored text of your secret key. This key, recall, is encrypted with your PGP passphrase. It can now be added to the secret key ring on the target system.

Public Key Management

P GP contains a clever, efficient, interlocking set of functions and formats to provide effective confidentiality and authentication services. To complete the system, one final area needs to be addressed: public-key management. In the PGP documentation, Phil Zimmermann neatly captures the importance of this area:

> This whole business of protecting public keys from tampering is the single most difficult problem in practical public key applications. It is the "Achilles heel" of public key cryptography, and a lot of software complexity is tied up in solving this one problem.

Because PGP is intended for use in a variety of formal and informal environments, no rigid key management scheme is set up; rather, PGP provides a structure for solving key management problems that enables a variety of flexible solutions. The hallmark of the PGP approach is that it doesn't rely on some central authority that must be trusted. However, a trusted central authority isn't precluded but is merely one of a number of options.

This chapter covers what you need to know about PGP in a system-independent way. Part II shows how to apply the principles of key management to specific PGP implementations.

First, how can keys be exchanged securely? Section 6.1 covers the various approaches. Next, how can one know a public key is valid? The solution is a technique known as public-key certification, which is examined in Section 6.2. Then, Section 6.3 clarifies the concepts of key legitimacy and key trust.

6.1 EXCHANGING PUBLIC KEYS

Suppose Bob and Alice decide to exchange public keys so they can communicate securely. Well, public keys are supposed to be public, so this should be easy. The parties could do the following:

1. Bob sends his public key to Alice by e-mail.
2. Alice sends her public key to Bob by e-mail.

Bob and Alice are now ready to communicate securely.

The Man in the Middle Attack

The problem with this simplistic approach is that it leaves both parties open to what is known as a man-in-the-middle attack. Here is how the bad guy (BG) can thwart the exchange (Figure 6.1):

1. Bob sends his public key out in an e-mail message addressed to Alice.
2. BG intercepts this message. BG saves Bob's public key and sends a message to Alice that has Bob's User ID but BG's public key. This message is sent in such a way that it appears as though it was sent from Bob's host system; that is, the return address on the e-mail message is BobP@university.edu. Alice receives BG's message and stores BG's public key with Bob's User ID and e-mail address.
3. Alice then sends her public key out in an e-mail message addressed to Bob.
4. BG intercepts Alice's message. BG saves Alice's public key and sends a message to Bob that has Alice's User ID but BG's public key. This message is sent in such a way that it appears as though it was sent from Alice's host system; that is, the return address on the e-mail message is alice@place.com. Bob receives BG's message and stores BG's public key with Alice's User ID and e-mail address.

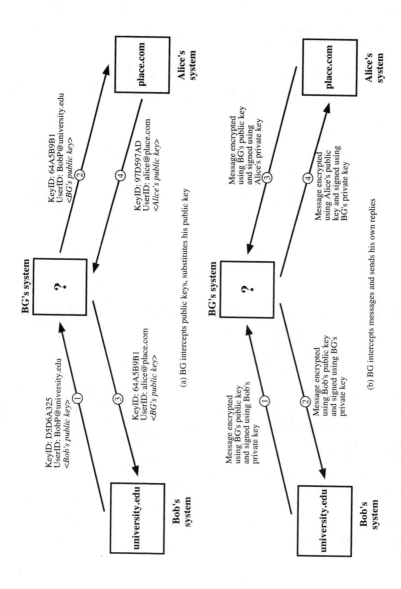

Fig **6.1**   A Man-in-the-Middle Attack

If BG can continue to intercept all messages between Bob and Alice, he can read them all. Furthermore, BG can send a message to Bob apparently signed by Alice, and vice versa. This state of affairs could go unnoticed for a considerable period of time. Bob or Alice might only become suspicious if a genuine message got through, which would show that the recipient is holding an incorrect public key (signature doesn't verify) and/or that the sender is holding an incorrect public key (unable to decrypt message).

How could BG get in such a position? There are a number of possibilities. For example, if Bob is using a shared system to hook into the Internet, such as a UNIX system, then BG could be someone with "superuser" privileges on the system. It wouldn't be too difficult for such a person to divert all incoming and outgoing traffic from Bob's mailbox to a special file. BG could also have access to a router, mail bridge, or other type of gateway through which all traffic between Bob and Alice must pass. Again, BG could use his privileged status on the gateway to intercept mail and to create and send mail with a fraudulent return address.

We can now see more clearly what the requirement is for the security of a public key. Despite the fact that a public key is to be, and must be, public, one needs to ensure that the association between a particular User ID and a particular key is valid. In other words if you have a key with a Key ID of D5D6A325 and a User ID of Bob Person <BobP@university.edu>, you need to know with certainty that this is Bob Person's public key whose e-mail address is BobP@university.edu. This will assure you that Bob Person created this public key and possesses the corresponding secret key.

How can one know such a thing with certainty? There are two ways to attack this problem. The first is to devise a secure means to exchange public keys, and the second is key certification. We examine the issue of secure exchange in the remainder of this section and look at key certification in Section 6.2.

It is important to note that these two approaches are complementary rather than either/or alternatives. Both approaches are important tools in the secure use of PGP.

Physical Exchange

The most secure means of public key exchange is the actual physical exchange of keys. Suppose that Bob and Alice are within a reasonable distance from each other. Then each could prepare a diskette with his or her public key on it, in ASCII armor format. The two then exchange diskettes. Alice loads the key from Bob's diskette and moves it onto her public key ring, and Bob does the same with Alice's key. If Bob and Alice know each other by sight, then a secure exchange has been achieved.

If the distances are too great, another possibility is simply to mail the diskettes containing the public keys. Of course, the mail distribution and delivery system isn't invulnerable to penetration, so this isn't a guaranteed channel. Security could be increased by using multiple channels. For example, Bob could mail a diskette with his public key to Alice and also send an e-mail message with his public key to Alice. Alice then compares the two keys and accepts them if they are identical. It would be very difficult for the same opponent to intercept the keys through both channels.

Telephone Verification Using Public-Key Fingerprints

The use of multiple channels, however, is somewhat clumsy. An attractive alternative to increasing the security of exchanges is to exploit something known as the public-key fingerprint. First we define the fingerprint and then see how it can be used in an exchange.

Public-Key Fingerprints   The fingerprint of a public key is simply the 128-bit MD5 hash code of that key. PGP can display the fingerprint of any public key in hexadecimal format. Each hexadecimal digit is 4 bits, so 32 hexadecimal digits represents a fingerprint. For example, here is the fingerprint of Alice's public key:

74 78 A4 84 CC 6B 98 66 39 85 45 AE 58 76 E8 7E

HEXADECIMAL NOTATION

Hexadecimal notation is widely used to represent computer-based data. Binary digits are grouped into sets of 4 bits. Each possible combination of 4 bits is given a symbol, as follows:

0000 = 0	0100 = 4	1000 = 8	1100 = C
0001 = 1	0101 = 5	1001 = 9	1101 = D
0010 = 2	0110 = 6	1010 = A	1110 = E
0011 = 3	0111 = 7	1011 = B	1111 = F

Since 16 symbols are used, the notation is called hexadecimal, and the
16 symbols are the hexadecimal digits.

The fingerprint of a public key is, for all practical purposes,
unique. The probability two different public keys having the same
fingerprint is less than 2^{-64}, or about 5×10^{-20}.

Telephone Verification   The public-key fingerprint provides
a convenient tool for telephone verification of public keys. Consider
the following scenario. Alice transmits her public key to Bob by e-
mail. Bob generates the fingerprint for that key and then calls
Alice and asks her to dictate the fingerprint over the phone. If Bob
can recognize Alice's voice and if the two fingerprints match, the
key is verified.

Key Repositories

Because public keys are intended to be public, it makes sense
to provide a repository or directory of public keys that is readily
accessible via e-mail or file transfer protocol (ftp). A public repository eases the task of distribution; if the repository contains many
names, then a user can build up a large collection of public keys
simply by extracting those he or she needs from a repository. This
still leaves open the question of how to ensure the validity of public keys obtained by this means. The most effective technique is
key certification, which is discussed in Section 6.2.

Two basic types of repositories are available for PGP users:
open public key servers and controlled public key databases. For
now, we provide a brief description of these two types; Chapter 15
provides more detail on how to use public key servers.

Public Key Servers   A public key server is a giant public
key ring with a simple e-mail interface for retrieving public keys
and updating the key ring. Anyone can add their public key to the
ring. Anyone can send a query to the server to retrieve a given key
by User ID or Key ID, a set of keys matching a particular portion
of a User ID or Key ID, or all the keys in the entire ring.

Public key servers on the Internet are interlocked: If you
send your key to one server, it is automatically passed on to other

servers on the Internet. Therefore, to determine whether a public
key is available, it is necessary to query only a single server.

Public key servers take no responsibility for the validity of
the keys on their rings; anyone can present a public key with its
associated User ID. Thus, some other means of verifying the public
key is wise. For example, the fingerprint of a key obtained from
the server could be verified with the alleged owner by telephone,
mail, or e-mail. It is up to the user to judge whether any of these
means is sufficient. A more attractive alternative is key certification, discussed in Section 6.2.

Public Key Database   A public key database is similar to a
public key server in that it serves as a repository of public keys.
The principal difference is that the provider of the public key database requires some proof of identity in order to guarantee the
validity of the key. One example of such a service is the Stable
Large Email Database (SLED), which is described in Chapter 15.

Closing Banner

Many operating systems and e-mail applications allow a user
to define a block of text that is automatically appended to any outgoing e-mail message and to any article posted on a USENET
newsgroup. This block is generally referred to as a *signature*; in
UNIX, the block is stored in a file in the user's directory with the
name *.signature*. To avoid confusion with the PGP signature, we
use the term *closing banner* instead.

Closing banners range from the serious to the humorous and
from the straightforward to the artistic. Some people use the closing banner as a way to express their personality or simply to make
some sort of statement, political or otherwise. A growing number
of people use the closing banner to convey PGP information.

As an example, Figure 6.2 shows Alice's closing banner.
Among the information therein contained is Alice's public key fingerprint. The banner also indicates that Alice's key may be obtained from SLED.

Why would Alice place her fingerprint in her closing banner?
From what has already been said, you know that it is possible to

```
| Alice Smith           | PGP fingerprint:           | public key available from
| Independent Consultant | 74 78 A4 84 CC 6B 98 66   | Stable Large Email
| P. O. Box 99999       | 39 85 45 AE 58 76 E8 7E    | Database.
| New York, NY 12345    | finger alice@place.com     | Contact info@Four11.com
```

Fig **6.2**   Alice's Closing Banner

impersonate Alice in either an e-mail message or a USENET posting, so anyone reading this closing banner cannot be sure that the information is authentic. Although Alice's PGP fingerprint in a closing banner isn't guaranteed to be authentic, it is useful as one element in the overall process of obtaining Alice's public key. Suppose Bob had seen this fingerprint on a number of Alice's USENET postings and then he obtains her public key from a server. If the fingerprint from that public key matches the one Bob has already obtained, this increases the degree of confidence Bob has that this is in fact Alice's key.

Why not simply call Alice and use the telephone exchange method outlined earlier? Bob may not know Alice and may never have heard her voice. Bob may not even have ever corresponded with Alice but wishes to initiate a secure correspondence. Under the circumstances, any means of increasing Bob's confidence in the validity of Alice's key is welcome.

The finger Command

A program called *finger* is available on many shared systems connected to the Internet and to other networks. This program can be used to obtain information on users and, in some cases, on resources on the host computer. For example, if someone on the same host as Bob Person executes the command

```
finger BobP
```

then the finger program is invoked and returns information on Bob. More significant, for our purposes, is the fact that the finger program is capable of invoking another finger program remotely and retrieving information. Thus, if someone running on some other system executes the command

```
finger BobP@university.edu
```

the local finger program will send a command to the finger program on Bob's computer and receive Bob's information in return.

Figure 6.3 is an example of the type of information returned by finger. It typically includes the person's login name and real name and whether the person is currently logged on. This type of information is automatically provided by the host. Additional information may be included if it has been entered by the user. On UNIX systems, this additional information is stored in the .plan file in the user's directory and shows up in the finger output preceded by the word *Plan*. In our example, Bob has included his title and address, an alternative e-mail address, and his PGP public key.

In Figure 6.2, Alice indicates in her closing banner that she has also included her public key in her .plan file, with the entry "finger alice@place.com."

Again, as with the use of the closing banner, the validity of the information in finger output is not guaranteed. Anyone with superuser privileges on a UNIX system can alter a user's .plan file. As with the closing banner, the information in a finger output is one more element that can increase confidence in a key's validity.

Please note that finger output isn't always available remotely. Many systems, particularly commercial systems, allow only local access to the finger program, for security reasons. Typically, educational and unclassified government computers will allow remote access.

6.2 CERTIFYING PUBLIC KEYS

For most PGP users, the physical exchange of public keys is usually impractical. Telephone verification is only practical and secure in a limited number of cases. Other tools, such as closing banners and finger output, aren't trustworthy by themselves. Something more is needed to make PGP practical as a universal secure e-mail capability. That additional tool is known as the public key certificate.[1]

A public key certificate is, in essence, a public key together with a User ID with an attached signature. The signer is testifying that the User ID associated with this public key is valid. Let us look at the structure of these certificates in PGP and then discuss how they are used.

PGP Public Key Certificates

The essential elements of a public-key certificate are:

- The public key itself
- A time stamp indicating when the public/secret key pair was generated
- A User ID for the public key
- Zero or more signatures for the public key and User ID

As an option, there may be additional User IDs associated with the key, and each of these User IDs may have associated signatures.

The relationship between public keys, User IDs, and signatures is best explained with an example. Figure 6.4 shows the structure of Bob's public key. Associated with the key itself are a key ID, derived from the public key, and a time stamp. These items are independent of the User ID and "belong" to the public key. Also associated with this key are the two User IDs that Bob has assigned to this key, reflecting the two e-mail addresses that he uses. The first User ID assigned by Bob is

```
Bob Person <BobP@university.edu>
```

Associated with this User ID are two signatures, one from Alice and one from Bob. At first glance, it may seem curious that Bob would sign his own key. Let's put that discussion off for a bit and first concentrate on Alice's signature.

First, what does it mean to sign a public key? Recall that

---

[1] The concept of public key certificates was first proposed in a bachelor's thesis (Kohnfelder, L. *Towards a Practical Public-Key Cryptosystem*, MIT, May 1978). Because of the importance of public-key certificates, this is by far the most frequently-referenced bachelor's thesis in the security literature and certainly one of the most frequently-referenced bachelor's theses in any discipline.

```
Login name: BobP                In real life: Robert Person
Directory: /home/BobP              Shell: /bin/tcsh
On since Jul 21 19:19:48 on ttym09
No unread mail
Plan:
Bob Person
Professor of Cryptology
Secret University
Alternate email address: RPerson@company.com

-----BEGIN PGP PUBLIC KEY BLOCK-----
Version: 2.6

mQCPAi4pFRsAAAEEAKgix5G3Ovg3hrI/vcMO5B5/jJRQQTb4AbYrwsbPtLY33NnG
TWx6XyvlYgoxxMbBEJXxPEa+5A5nfJkU0KsyBjhdsFfR5DWL1lt5u529kxmUPw6m
XaDe/8j9iyIZv+x8jmbDE/uYsmd570AxfdoYpZrotaxkcbpoag/8z+rV1qM1ABEB
AAG0IEJvYiBQZXJzb24gPEPEJvYlBAdW5pdmMyc21oeS51ZHU+iQCVAgUQLjFnK7xj
u8KX1ZetAQFp3QP/SvsaEWTYsOvYXlo8FX6N8Z2O5tupMAh+Z4sSYu7NNBhz1Q3u
dBrxBh695Sm4bTEbzrmvYVUdPY6JYTZcaiAZ8uFy9xjUUmbw4D9LFfUqq17OO/1R
mwuUyEtX+o9Jq2Vgppnuxr89zzYi/1Wkz4HVaojJKHws7NYQoantnsVXZZqJAJUC
BRAuKnZ6D/zP6tXWoyUBAbxQBACKSjnaEg7OkKi4UFN0JdbnprJjTjGKVCOBnTyC
LqWUUrVIRI8Yo9YelQF0PP1go0rgF9S1J65RJS31gaLxyqqPnxj/mPOFsab26Y3Q
jRkkCkGnKCVQs2RiluX/2Fpsd8Lt1Pxs+41T35uTBs42b3Qm4+vzuNT+KgyqRyDY
t2CyprQkUm9iZXJ0IFBlcnNvbiA8Ul81BlcnNvbkBjb21wYW55LmNvbT4+iQCVAgUQ
LjFlcw/8z+rV1qM1AQGatQP/Xjk5bsdYdNHJEHWLYl1j/jwxbgcLt1bN8VUCIvPJ
vQyIAUKDTTEGb+deDfFRfEbrLyLTR6FFcJJs3QfiBoktc4rNcONGKpGII8UkLZ4+
n98a4Uqo+e5ozz1KJijh+2NDHBoKPY5ZBcDZX9FOAyzFFoEbb6HpOEm5NZuF2Xdc
9Ls=
=Rw9Y
-----END PGP PUBLIC KEY BLOCK-----
```

Fig 6.3   Output of Command "finger BobP @ university.edu"

a signature on a message is formed by taking the MD5 hash code
of the entire message and then encrypting that with the secret
key of the signature. Anyone can verify that this message has
been signed by this person by using the appropriate public key.

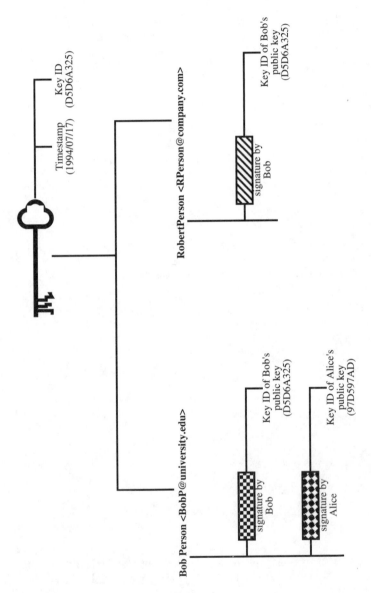

Fig 6.4   Structure of Bob Person's Public Key

Furthermore, everyone is guaranteed that the file hasn't been altered; otherwise the signature would be invalid. This process of signing can be applied to any block of data. In the case of a public key, the actual public key itself, together with an associated User ID, constitutes the input to the MD5 algorithm. Then the signer's secret key is used to encrypt the MD5 hash code. Figure 6.5 is an example. Suppose Bob has created his public key, assigned two User IDs, and then signed each public-key/User-ID combination. This entire key is then presented to Alice. Alice signs the combination of Bob's public key and the first User ID (Bob Person <BobP@university.edu>). The result:

1. Alice is stating that she believes that this public key belongs to Bob Person <BobP@university.edu> and that Bob is in possession of the corresponding secret key.
2. Anyone can verify that Alice has in fact signed this key by using Alice's public key to check her signature (Figure 6.6).
3. If a user, say Ted, has Alice's public key and verifies her signature of Bob's key, then Ted knows:
   (a) Alice is testifying to the validity of the association between this key and the User ID (Bob Person <BobP@university.edu>).
   (b) No one has tampered with either the public key or the User ID.

Therefore, if Ted is sure that he has a valid public key from Alice and if he trusts her to testify in this matter, then Ted can have confidence that he has a valid copy of Bob's public key. If Ted has many correspondents, then this matter of trust and confidence may be difficult to keep track of. Fortunately, PGP provides some useful tools for managing trust and confidence, and we will look at those in Section 6.3. But first, we need to complete our exploration of the implications of public-key certificates.

Viewing Signatures

It is a simple matter to see the signatures attached to the various keys on your public key ring. When PGP displays your key ring or a part of it, you can specify that signatures also be displayed.

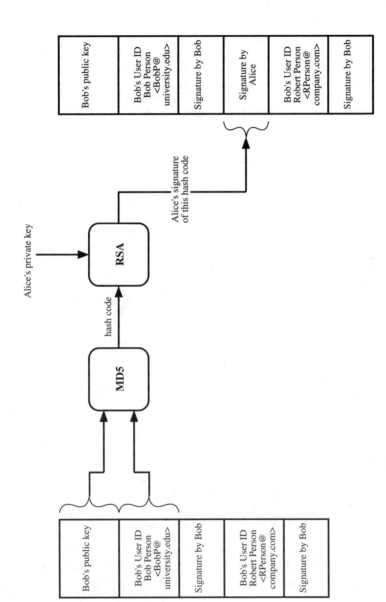

Fig **6.5**   Alice Signs Bob's Public Key

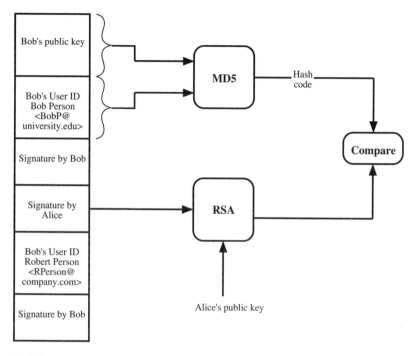

Fig **6.6**   Verifying Alice's Signature

Figure 6.7 shows Bob's public key ring, with signatures. Before examining the signatures, note that there are two changes in Bob's key ring since we saw it in Chapter 5 (Figure 5.2). First, Bob has moved his key up. This was accomplished, as we explained in Chapter 5, by removing Bob's public key and then adding it back to the ring. After this was done, Bob added Alice's public key to his ring. It is also evident that Bob updated his own public key to include Alice's signature.

Bob's public key reflects the structure in Figure 6.4: there are two User IDs; Bob and Alice have both signed the first User ID, and Bob has signed the second User ID.

Most of the other keys on the ring have signatures. Each signature includes both the encrypted hash code that is the essence of the signature and the Key ID of the key's signer. When PGP displays Bob's ring with signatures, it looks up each of these Key IDs

```
Key ring: 'Macintosh HD:Bob:pubring.pgp'
Type bits/keyID          Date         User ID
pub    1024/97D597AD     1994/07/19   Alice Smith <alice@place.com>
sig         D5D6A325                  Bob Person <BobP@university.edu>
sig         97D597AD                  Alice Smith <alice@place.com>
pub    1024/D5D6A325     1994/07/17   Bob Person <BobP@university.edu>
sig         97D597AD                  Alice Smith <alice@place.com>
sig         D5D6A325                  Bob Person <BobP@university.edu>
                                      Robert Person
                                          <RPerson@company.com>
sig         D5D6A325                  Bob Person <BobP@university.edu>
pub    1024/5F63A5B9     1994/02/08   Stable Large Email Database
                                          <sled@drebes.com>
sig         5F63A5B9                  Stable Large Email Database
                                          <sled@drebes.com>
pub    1024/CB768501     1993/10/13   ViaCrypt <Phone (602) 944-0773>
sig         C7A966DD                  Philip R. Zimmermann
                                          <prz@acm.org>
sig         CB768501                  ViaCrypt <Phone (602) 944-0773>
                                      ViaCrypt
                                      <70304.41@compuserve.com>
                                      ViaCrypt <viacrypt@acm.org>
sig         67ECF13D                  (Unknown signator, can't be
                                          checked)
                                      ViaCrypt <FAX (602) 943-2601>
pub     512/4D0C4EE1     1992/09/10   Jeffrey I. Schiller <jis@mit.edu>
sig         C7A966DD                  Philip R. Zimmermann <prz@acm.org>
sig         8DCBB1C3                  (Unknown signator, can't be
                                          checked)
sig         71946BDF                  (Unknown signator, can't be
                                          checked)
sig         7396D3B7                  (Unknown signator, can't be
                                          checked)


                                                          (continued)
```

Fig **6.7**   Bob's Public Key Ring, Showing Signatures

```
sig        8CB4B951                        (Unknown signator, can't be
                                           checked)
pub        1024/0778338D    1993/09/17     Philip L. Dubois <dubois@csn.org>
sig        C7A966DD                        Philip R. Zimmermann
                                           <prz@acm.org>
pub        1024/FBBB8AB1    1994/05/07     Colin Plumb <colin@nyx.cs.du.edu>
sig        C7A966DD                        Philip R. Zimmermann
                                           <prz@acm.org>
sig        865AA7F3                        (Unknown signator, can't be
                                           checked)
sig        FBBB8AB1                        Colin Plumb
                                           <colin@nyx.cs.du.edu>
pub        1024/C7A966DD    1993/05/21     Philip R. Zimmermann
                                           <prz@acm.org>
sig        C7A966DD                        Philip R. Zimmermann
                                           <prz@acm.org>
sig        FF67F70B                        (Unknown signator, can't be
                                           checked)
pub        709/C1B06AF1     1992/09/25     Derek Atkins <warlord@MIT.EDU>
sig        C7A966DD                        Philip R. Zimmermann
                                           <prz@acm.org>
pub        1024/8DE722D9    1992/07/22     Branko Lankester
                                           <branko@hacktic.nl>
sig        C7A966DD                        Philip R. Zimmermann
                                           <prz@acm.org>
sig        8DE722D9                        Branko Lankester
                                           <branko@hacktic.nl>
pub        1024/9D997D47    1992/08/02     Peter Gutmann
                                           <pgut1@cs.aukuni.ac.nz>
sig        C7A966DD                        Philip R. Zimmermann
                                           <prz@acm.org>
pub        510/DC620423     1992/08/27     Jean-loup Gailly
                                           <jloup@chorus.fr>
pub        1024/28748E05    1992/09/06     Hugh A.J. Kennedy <70042.
                                           710@compuserve.com>
13 matching keys found.
```

Fig **6.7**   Bob's Public Key Ring, Showing Signatures *(continued)*

in this public key ring. If a match is found, then the User ID of the signer is displayed. Otherwise, PGP indicates that this is an unknown signature. For example, Phil Zimmermann's key (Key ID = C7A966DD) is included in this ring. Therefore, every time that Phil's Key ID appears on a signature, PGP displays Phil's User ID.

How Big Is a Public Key?

You will notice that some public keys that you see (in ASCII armor) are much bigger than others. This is primarily due to the number of signatures. For example, compare the print-out of Bob's public key in Figure 5.4 to that in Figure 6.3. The first version was prepared by Bob before he read Chapter 6, so it contains no signatures. Bob subsequently added his own signature and that of Alice before putting his key in his .plan file.

Incidentally, don't confuse the role of the User ID with that of the Key ID with respect to key signing. For example, Bob has two User IDs associated with his public key and has signed both of them. It would appear that in both cases Bob has signed as (Bob Person <BobP@university.edu>), rather than signing as (Robert Person <RPerson@company.com>). This isn't correct. When Bob signs anything, he signs using his secret key. There may be more than one User ID associated with the corresponding public key, but there is only one public key and only one secret key in this key pair. When PGP displays signatures, it shows the Key ID and, if available, a User ID. PGP simply picks the first User ID associated with a particular public key for display purposes.

On the other hand, it does make a difference where the signatures go. Looking at Figure 6.7, we see that Alice has testified that the person identified as (Bob Person <BobP @ university.edu>) is the owner of public key D5D6A325. Alice makes no claims about the identity (Robert Person <RPerson @ company.com>)

The Use of Certificates in Public-Key Exchange The use of signatures on public keys has far-reaching implications. This practice makes widespread use of public-key applications, such as PGP, possible. It is a testimony to the flexibility and power of public-key cryptography that a public-key technique (key signing) can be used to solve the most difficult practical problem (key distribution) in public-key applications.

There are essentially two different ways to exploit public-key certificates for PGP key exchange: person-to-person exchange and key repository access.

Person-to-Person Exchange   Suppose Ted needs Bob's public key but doesn't know Bob or have any convenient way to verify Bob's key. If Ted has Alice's public key and trusts her to certify other keys, then the sequence of Figure 6.8(a) will do the job. At some point, Bob and Alice have exchanged keys in a mutually satisfactory manner. Bob knows that Alice is well known among people with whom he may wish to correspond and that most of those people are likely to have Alice's key. Therefore Bob asks Alice to sign his key and return it. Bob can then add Alice's signature to his public key on his public key ring. Now, if Ted asks Bob for a copy of his public key, Bob sends the key that is signed by Alice. Because Ted trusts Alice to sign keys, Ted accepts Bob's key as valid.

In effect, Alice has introduced Bob to Ted. The more people that Ted trusts to act as introducers, the easier it will be for him to build up a collection of valid public keys on his public key ring.

Key Repositories   A public key server is a handy place to find lots of public keys. Servers currently on the Internet maintain thousands of keys. A company, professional organization, or special interest group could set up their own server. However, as we mentioned, servers take no responsibility for the validity of keys; they merely serve as repositories.

It is key signatures that make public key servers useful. Figure 6.8(b) shows a typical use of such a server. After Bob has obtained Alice's signature on his key, he posts it on a public key server. Later, Ted retrieves Bob's key. Because Bob's key is signed by Alice, Ted accepts it as genuine.

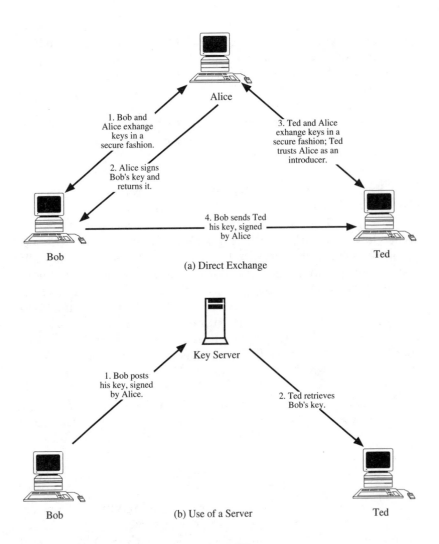

Fig **6.8**   Techniques for Exchanging Signed Keys

Don't Sign if You Are Not Sure

Unless you are absolutely convinced of the validity of a public-key/User-ID combination, do NOT sign it and send it back out to any server or individual. Later on, someone may rely on your say-so and accept an invalid key.

Signing Your Own Key

Always sign your own key. Period. End of debate. It would be a good exercise for you to put the book aside now and try to figure out *why* you should sign your key.

Have you figured it out? Well look at the following key, prepared by Bob:

```
pub   1024/97D597AD 1994/07/19 Alice Smith
              <alice@university.edu>
```

Compare this to Bob's public key ring. This item is Alice's public key. We know that because of the Key ID. However, Bob has altered Alice's User ID. Bob cannot do this type of modification from within PGP: PGP only allows you to edit User IDs on public keys for which you have the corresponding secret key. But if Bob knows the data structure of a public key, this modification is a simple matter.

Let us suppose Bob has set things up on the university.edu system so that mail coming in for Alice is directed to a mailbox that he controls. Bob posts this modified key to a public key server. Now, anyone who uses such a key server as a kind of e-mail address book will send Bob mail intended for Alice. Of course, Bob can't read the mail if it is encrypted, but then, neither can Alice because she never receives the message. At minimum, Bob has created a temporary disruption.

If Alice had signed her key, this type of fraud would not be successful; as soon as Bob modifies Alice's User ID, Alice's signature on this key is no longer valid.

Key Revocation

If you suspect for any reason that your secret key has been compromised, you need to revoke your public key. You also need to revoke your public key if you forget your passphrase. In either case, you need to get the word out to your correspondents and potential correspondents, so they will stop using your obsolete public key.

The security issues for revoking a key are much the same as for supplying a key in the first place: The recipient needs to be assured that the key revocation message is valid and not an attempt by someone else to disrupt communications. Once again, the power and flexibility of public-key encryption provides a simple solution.

Key Revocation Certificates   To revoke a public key, the owner of that key creates a key revocation certificate. This is simply a copy of the public key, including the Key ID and associated User IDs, plus a tag indicating that this is a key revocation certificate, all signed with the owner's corresponding secret key. If anyone receives such a certificate, they know that it can only have been created by someone in possession of the corresponding secret key. This can be checked in the same way as a signature on a public-key certificate (Figure 6.6).

Three cases are of concern here:

Case 1: Attempt to Disrupt Operations

A bad guy (BG) tries to disrupt Bob's operations by revoking his key, although BG hasn't managed to lay his hands on Bob's secret key. It can't be done. Because BG doesn't have Bob's secret key, BG cannot sign the necessary key revocation certificate.

Case 2: Secret Key Acquired

BG manages to steal a copy of Bob's secret key ring and manages to discover Bob's secret key (Bob didn't follow all my advice on protecting passphrases) or else BG manages to discover Bob's secret key by cryptanalysis (use a big key to prevent this). Until Bob discovers this disaster, BG is in a position to make mischief. Of course, BG is also in a position to revoke Bob's key, but that is something Bob will do anyway once he discovers the problem.

Case 3: Bob Loses His Secret Key or Forgets His Passphrase

Under these circumstances, Bob should immediately revoke his public key.

Preparing a Revocation Certificate in Advance   If Bob no longer has his secret key, how can he prepare the revocation certificate? Good point. If you recall, you were advised to store a copy of your secret key on a backup diskette and to make a hard copy. I would also recommend preparing a revocation certificate and keeping a copy of it on your backup diskette, as well as keeping a hard copy.

If you do create a key revocation certificate for possible future use, beware of the risks involved. To create a revocation certificate you must use your passphrase to verify it is really you doing the revocation. Once you extract the certificate and print it out, it is no longer protected by a passphrase and anyone can use it.

Finally, you need to be careful how you prepare the revocation certificate. When you issue a command to PGP to revoke a key, PGP defaults to the your public key ring. If you now revoke your public key, there is no way to "unrevoke" it and the key remains on your public key ring in an unusable state. To avoid this problem, do the following:

1. Copy your (not yet revoked) public key to another file, say an ASCII-armored file. You need this anyway to send your public key to others.
2. Revoke your key on your public key ring.
3. Copy the (now revoked) key to a backup file that will be saved in a secure place.
4. Remove the revoked key from your key ring.
5. Add your public key back to your key ring from the file generated in step 1.

The Effect of Key Revocation   If your secret key is compromised or lost, you should post a key revocation certificate to all public key servers containing your public key and also send it to any correspondents. When PGP receives such a certificate, it adds it to the public key ring. If the affected key isn't on the ring, the revocation certificate is simply added to the ring. If the affected key is on the ring, then the revocation certificate is linked with that key. If a key has been revoked, PGP will not allow its use to encrypt messages to that user. If an incoming signature uses the key, PGP will warn the user that this key has been revoked.

If you receive a key revocation certificate, you can either add it to your public key ring or simply delete the affected key. The latter course keeps your key ring smaller, but I advise against it. At some later time, you may receive a copy of the revoked key, with one or more very trustworthy signatures attached. You might forget that this key has been revoked (can you really remember a Key ID?) and add this key to your ring in good faith.

Changing Your User ID

Most people, quite rightly, include their e-mail address as part of their User ID. If there comes a time when your e-mail address changes, you will want to update your public key to include a User ID with your new address. Unfortunately, this process interacts with the key signatures.

Recall that a signature applies not to a public key alone but to the combination of a public key and a User ID. Therefore, if you add a new User ID to your public key on a key server, only the old ID will remain signed. To maintain the same level of certification on the new User ID you must have the key with this User ID resigned by all the people who signed the old User ID.

If you want to change your existing User ID, and not simply add a new one, it is a two-step process:

1. Add the new User ID to your public key.
2. Remove the old User ID. PGP will ask if you want to remove the whole key. Say no, and PGP will then walk through each User ID on the key, giving you the option of deleting it. When a User ID is removed, all the signatures attached to it are also removed.

6.3 OWNER TRUST AND KEY LEGITIMACY

When Ted uses PGP to send and receive e-mail, his PGP program makes heavy use of his public key ring. For example: When Ted sends a message to Alice, PGP uses Alice's public key in the message encryption process; when Ted receives a message from Bob, PGP uses Bob's public key to verify the signature. This brings up the fundamental question to be asked about any public key PGP uses, the question of key legitimacy:

KEY LEGITIMACY

Do I believe this is a valid public key for this User ID?

Ultimately, it is the responsibility of each user to answer this question for each key on his or her public key ring. PGP goes a long way toward automating this process by providing a set of tools for exploiting public key certificates.

Some of the keys on Ted public key ring have signatures attached to them. If, for example, Ted has Bob's public key, which is signed by Alice, and Ted trusts Alice to act as an introducer, then Ted will accept that key/User-ID combination as valid. Rather than make Ted think this through each time, the process can be automated by enabling Ted to tell PGP whether or not Alice is trusted to act as an introducer. For this purpose, PGP uses the concept of owner trust.

OWNER TRUST

Do I trust this user to sign other public keys?

This area of trust and legitimacy is perhaps the most complicated aspect of PGP. To help us understand it, we begin with an example.

The Relation Between Owner Trust and Key Legitimacy

Recall the structure of Bob's public key shown in Figure 6.4. This is the information that is contained in a copy of Bob's key that is conveyed in ASCII armor from one user to another or that is stored on a public key server. When this key is stored on a user's public key ring, it contains additional information relating to legitimacy and trust.

Let us suppose that Ted gets a copy of Bob's key from a public key server and stores it on his ring, as illustrated in Figure 6.9. We can see that some new information has been added by the local PGP.

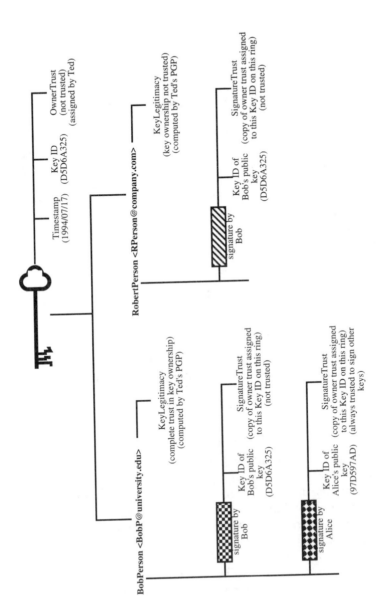

Fig 6.9   A Copy of Bob Person's Public Key Residing on Ted's Public Key Ring

When Ted instructs PGP to add this key to his ring, PGP will query Ted as to whether he trusts Bob to act as an introducer. The choices are:

- I don't know
- No
- Usually
- Yes, always

The answer doesn't necessarily reflect Ted's opinion of Bob's character. Ted may not know Bob even though he needs to correspond with him, and so has no definite opinion on this matter. Or, Ted may know Bob and assumes he is an honest, trustworthy person but questions whether Bob might be too casual in signing other people's keys. In this case, Ted might answer "No" or "Usually."

In the case where Ted knows Bob only very casually and isn't convinced that Bob treats the key certification responsibility with the respect it deserves, he answers "No." Accordingly, PGP associates an OwnerTrust parameter with this key of "not trusted." That means that if PGP encounters a key that is signed by Bob, it ignores Bob's signature. This lack of trust in Bob's key for certification purposes will remain the state of affairs until Ted explicitly changes the OwnerTrust parameter on Bob's key.

A separate question is whether or not this key actually belongs to the individual known to Ted as Bob Person whose e-mail address is BobP@university.edu. Prior to adding Bob's key to his public key ring, Ted had added Alice's key and indicated to PGP that he would always trust her to sign other keys. When PGP adds Bob's key to the ring, it looks up, on Ted's public key ring, the Key ID of each signature attached to Bob's key. For each Key ID that is found, the OwnerTrust value for the owner is transferred to a SignatureTrust parameter assigned to the signature.

In this case the only signature, other than Bob's, attached to Bob's key is the signature formed using the key with the ID of 97D597AD. PGP determines that this key belongs to Alice, and that Alice's OwnerTrust is "always trusted." So, since Alice is always trusted by Ted, a SignatureTrust value of "always trusted" is attached to Alice's signature on Ted's key.

Once PGP has determined the signature trust values of all the signatures on Bob's key, it can determine the legitimacy of each User-ID/key combination for that key. Because Alice is always trusted to certify keys and she has signed the first User ID on Bob's key, PGP declares that it has complete trust that (Bob Person <BobP@university.edu>) is the actual owner of this key. No trustworthy signature appears on the other User ID, so that User ID isn't assigned complete trust.

Trust and Legitimacy Values Are Local

All of the trust and legitimacy parameters associated with a public key on your public key ring ultimately derive from your personal assessment of the key owners. If you extract a key from your public key ring to send to someone else, PGP doesn't include the trust and legitimacy parameters. In other words, a stand-alone key, suitable for transmission to others, looks like Figure 6.4, whereas a key on a public key ring looks like Figure 6.9.

Ultimate Trust

Any public key that was created by you (i.e., the corresponding secret key is on your secret key ring) is automatically considered by PGP to be completely trusted to sign other keys. PGP refers to this as "ultimate trust," because, ultimately, the trust assigned to any other key owner depends on you.

You do trust yourself, don't you?

Marginal Trust

When PGP asks you whether a key owner is trusted to sign other keys, one possible answer is "usually." Such an owner is considered to be "marginally trusted." By default, PGP will accept a User-ID/key as valid if two marginally trusted individuals sign it or if one fully trusted individual signs it. The user can adjust either of these parameters so that, for example, two fully trusted or four marginally trusted signers are required.

Examples

Figure 6.10 shows Ted's public key ring, with the trust parameters for each key. Note that Ted's own key is designated with the ultimate trust; any key signed by Ted is completely valid. An asterisk indicates the ultimately trusted key.

KeyID	Trust	Validity	User ID
D253C359	undefined	undefined	Joan Johnson <jj@nonprofit.org>
	undefined		Joan Johnson <jj@nonprofit.org>
* 1898832D	ultimate	complete	Ted Jones <Ted@elsewhere.net>
c	ultimate		Ted Jones <Ted@elsewhere.net>
97D597AD	complete	complete	Alice Smith <alice.place.com>
c	ultimate		Ted Jones <Ted@elsewhere.net>
c	complete		Alice Smith <alice.place.com>
D5D6A325	untrusted	complete	Bob Person
			<BobP@university.edu>
c	complete		Alice Smith <alice.place.com>
c	untrusted		Bob Person
			<BobP@university.edu>
	undefined		Robert Person
			<RPerson@company.com>
c	untrusted		Bob Person
			<BobP@university.edu>
4D0C4EE1	unknown	complete	Jeffrey I. Schiller
			<jis@mit.edu>
c	complete		Philip R. Zimmermann
			<prz@acm.org>
	undefined		(KeyID: 8DCBB1C3)
	undefined		(KeyID: 71946BDF)
	undefined		(KeyID: 7396D3B7)
	undefined		(KeyID: 8CB4B951)
C7A966DD	complete	complete	Philip R. Zimmermann
			<prz@acm.org>
c	ultimate		Ted Jones <Ted@elsewhere.net>
c	complete		Philip R. Zimmermann
			<prz@acm.org>
	undefined		(KeyID: FF67F70B)

Fig **6.10**   Ted's Public Key Ring, Showing Trust Levels

For each key on the ring, each User ID is shown, followed by
the signatures attached to the User-ID/key pair. Alice's key has
been signed by Ted, so Alice's key is completely valid; the same is

true for Phil Zimmermann's key. The entry for Alice's key indicates she is completely trusted to sign other keys. So we see that Bob's key with User ID (Bob Person <BobP@ university.edu>) is signed by Alice and is therefore completely valid. Note that this doesn't mean Bob is trusted to sign other keys; it only means that Ted's PGP believes that this key is valid and is therefore safe to use in message exchanges. Accordingly, we see that Bob's key with User ID (Robert Person <RPerson@company.com>) is listed with undefined validity because it is only signed by Bob, who is untrusted. A "c" marks any signature by a trusted signer.

Finally, Joan's key is listed with undefined validity and undefined trust. Even though PGP doesn't know if this key is valid, the key is maintained on the ring. If Ted sends a message to Joan, PGP will encrypt the session key with Joan's public key, but, because this public key is of undefined validity, PGP will first warn Ted of this fact and ask if he wishes to proceed. Similarly, if Ted receives a message from Joan, PGP will warn him that the key that must be used to check the signature is of undefined validity.

In some cases, a signature is prepared with a key that isn't known to Ted's PGP. That is, the Key ID of the signer doesn't match that of any key on the public key ring. In this case, PGP simply lists the signature as undefined trust and displays the Key ID.

Now look at Joan's public key ring (Figure 6.11). Joan has designated both Bob and Alice as marginally trustworthy. Joan has a copy of Ted's public key signed by both Bob and Alice. Therefore, Joan's PGP accepts Ted's key as completely valid.

Adding a Key

When a user adds a new key to his or her public key ring, PGP goes through the sequence of steps outlined in Figure 6.12. First, PGP checks to see if any of the signatures attached to this key were made using a key known to this PGP. If so, PGP then checks to see if the signature or signatures are sufficient to certify this key as completely valid. If a User-ID on the new public key is signed by one fully trusted key owner or two marginally trusted key owners, the key can be accepted as valid.

If the key isn't sufficiently certified, the PGP asks whether the user wishes to sign the key. If the user does so, the new User-ID/key is certified as completely valid.

```
KeyID        Trust      Validity    User ID
   1898832D  unknown    complete    Ted Jones <Ted@elsewhere.net>
c             marginal               Bob Person
                                        <BobP@university.edu>
c             marginal               Alice Smith <alice.place.com>
c             unknown                Ted Jones <Ted@elsewhere.net>
*  D253C359  ultimate   complete    Joan Johnson <jj@nonprofit.org>
c             ultimate               Joan Johnson <jj@nonprofit.org>
   97D597AD  marginal   complete    Alice Smith <alice.place.com>
c             ultimate               Joan Johnson <jj@nonprofit.org>
c             unknown                Ted Jones <Ted@elsewhere.net>
c             marginal               Alice Smith <alice.place.com>
   D5D6A32   marginal   complete    Bob Person
                                        <BobP@university.edu>
c             ultimate               Joan Johnson <jj@nonprofit.org>
c             marginal               Alice Smith <alice.place.com>
c             marginal               Bob Person
                                        <BobP@university.edu>
              marginal               Robert Person
                                        <RPerson@company.com>
c             marginal               Bob Person
                                        <BobP@university.edu>
```

Fig **6.**11   Joan's Public Key Ring, Showing Trust Levels

If the key is certified as valid, either by the user or by trusted signatures of other users, PGP prompts the user to assign a level of trust to the new key for signing other keys. If the key hasn't been certified as valid, then PGP isn't sure that this key really belongs to the advertised owner and will not ask for an assignment of owner trust.

Once all of this trust processing is completed, the new key is added to the key ring.

PGP Trust Model

Every time that you update your public key ring, PGP recomputes the trust parameters in the ring to achieve consistency. In

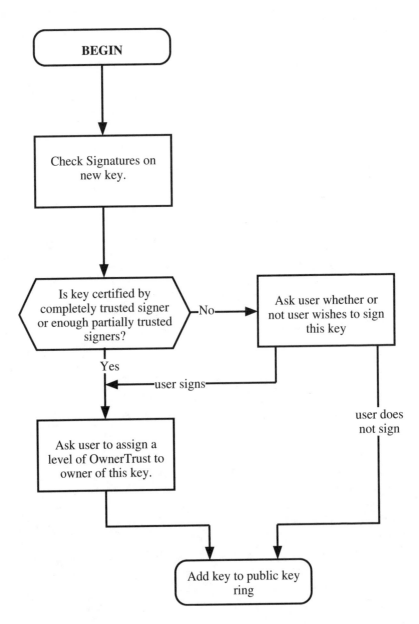

Fig **6.12**   Adding a Key to a Public Key Ring

essence, this is a top-down process. For each OwnerTrust field, PGP scans the ring for all signatures authored by that owner and updates the SigTrust field to equal the OwnerTrust field. This process starts with keys for which there is ultimate trust. All KeyLegit fields are then computed on the basis of the attached signatures.

Figure 6.13 shows the structure of a public-key ring and provides an example of the way in which signature trust and key legitimacy are related. The user has acquired a number of public keys, some directly from their owners and some from a third party such as a key server.

The node labeled You refers to the entry in the public-key ring corresponding to this user. This key is valid and the OwnerTrust value is ultimate trust. Each other node in the key ring has an OwnerTrust value of undefined unless some other value is assigned by the user. In this example, the user has specified that it always trusts users D, E, F, and L to sign other keys. This user also partially trusts users A and B to sign other keys.

The shading, or lack thereof, of the nodes in figure 6.13 indicate the level of trust assigned by this user. The tree structure indicates which keys have been signed by which other users. If a key is signed by a user whose key is also in this key ring, the arrow joins the signed key to the signer. If the key is signed by a user whose key isn't present in this key ring, the arrow joins the signed key to a question mark, indicating that the signer is unknown to the user.

Several points are illustrated in this figure:

1. Note that all keys whose owners are fully or partially trusted by the user have been signed by this user, with the exception of node L. Such a user signature isn't always necessary, as the presence of node L indicates, but in practice most users are likely to sign the keys for most owners that they trust. So, for example, even though E's key is already signed by trusted introducer F, the user chose to sign E's key directly.

2. We assume that two partially trusted signatures are sufficient to certify a key. Hence, the key for user H is deemed valid by PGP because it is signed by A and B, both of whom are partially trusted.

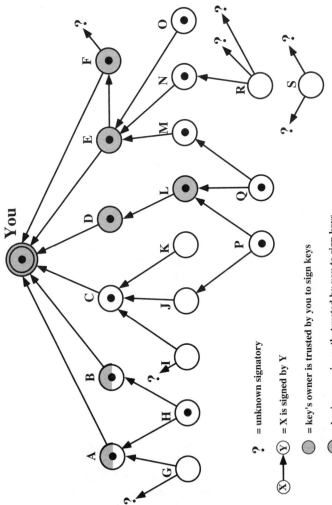

? = unknown signatory

 = X is signed by Y

= key's owner is trusted by you to sign keys

= key's owner is partly trusted by you to sign keys

= key is deemed legitimate by you

Fig 6.13   PGP Trust Model Example

3. A key may be determined to be valid because it is signed by one fully trusted or two partially trusted signers, but its user may not be trusted to sign other keys. For example, N's key is valid because it is signed by E, whom this user trusts, but N isn't trusted to sign other keys because this user hasn't assigned N that trust value. Therefore, although R's key is signed by N, PGP doesn't consider R's key valid. This situation makes perfect sense. If you wish to send a secret message to an individual, it isn't necessary that you trust that individual in any respect. It is only necessary that you are sure you have the correct public key for that individual.

4. Figure 6.13 also shows a detached "orphan" node S, with two unknown signatures. Such a key may have been acquired from a key server. PGP cannot assume that this key is valid simply because it came from a reputable server. The user must declare the key valid by signing it or by telling PGP that it is willing to fully trust one of the key's signers.

USING PGP

DOS PGP:
Getting Started

This chapter and the next examine the DOS implementation of PGP.[1] This chapter provides a step-by-step look at the basics. Follow the sequence of operations in this chapter and you will be ready to use PGP.

PGP IN A NUTSHELL

If you are reading this section first, before reading Part I, and you have no familiarity with PGP, please read this box. PGP (Pretty Good Privacy) is a software package that does two major things:

1. Provides confidentiality for messages sent by electronic mail: Only the sender and receiver can read the message.
2. Enables the sender to digitally sign a message so that the receiver knows that the message hasn't come from an impostor and hasn't been altered.

Both services rely on a scheme known as public-key encryption. The essence of this scheme is as follows: Everyone using PGP has two keys: one public key, which anyone is allowed to know, and one secret key, which is kept secret by the user.

Any message can be scrambled, or encrypted, in such a way that only the recipient can unscramble it. The sender performs a set of operations to encrypt the message that involves the use of the intended

---

[1] The examples displayed in this chapter were generated using ViaCrypt PGP 2.7. Other DOS versions have virtually the identical user interface.

recipient's public key. The recipient is then able to decrypt the message using his or her secret key.

Any message can be signed by performing an operation involving the signer's secret key. The signature can subsequently be checked by performing an operation involving the signer's public key. Therefore, when you send a message, you can sign it with your secret key, and any recipient can verify your signature using your public key.

To use PGP successfully, you must do three things:

1. Keep your secret key secret: Don't let anyone else learn it.
2. Make sure that all potential correspondents have your public key.
3. Get the public key of each potential correspondent.

7.1 GETTING STARTED

This chapter takes you through a series of steps following installation of DOS PGP on your system. The installation itself depends somewhat on which version of PGP you have. Once you are done with the installation, you should have at least the following files in the directory you use, which should be called C:\PGP.

- pgp.exe: The executable PGP program.
- config.txt: Contains some configuration parameters that can be used to tailor PGP's operation. For now, leave the default settings.
- keys.asc: Contains the public keys of some of PGP's developers.

Once you have started to use PGP, it generates five more files in the same directory:

- pubring.pgp: Your default public key ring.
- pubring.bak: Your default backup public key ring; PGP automatically updates this ring so that it is one change behind pubring.pgp.
- secring.pgp: Your default secret key ring.
- secring.bak: Your default backup secret key ring; PGP automatically updates this ring so that it is one change behind secring.pgp.
- randseed.bin: Used by PGP in the random-number generation process; you don't need to be concerned with it.

PGP operates in a somewhat unusual fashion for a DOS program. You don't load PGP into memory and then perform a series of commands. Rather, each command begins from the DOS prompt and involves typing pgp followed by various qualifiers and parameters. So, the first step is to change to your pgp directory. At any DOS prompt, type:

cd \pgp

DOS responds with

C:\pgp>

Now you are ready to go.[2]

7.2 KEY GENERATION

The first step is to generate a secret/public key pair. Type:

```
pgp -kg
```

The two letters following the dash indicate the type of command. The k indicates that this is a key management command, and the g indicates that this is the key generation command.

PGP responds with:

```
Current time: 1994/08/01 21:23 GMT
Pick your RSA key size:
  1)  512 bits- Low commercial grade, fast but
      less secure
  2)  768 bits- High commercial grade, medium
      speed, good security
  3)  1024 bits- "Military" grade, slow, highest
      security
Choose 1, 2, or 3, or enter desired number of bits:
```

[2] For the remainder of this chapter, all screen output will be shown inside a box.

As you can see, the larger the key size, the more secure will be your communication. It takes noticeably longer to generate larger keys, but key generation is a one-time procedure. The time to prepare messages for sending or to process received messages doesn't change much with the different key sizes. Therefore, always select option 3.

PGP responds:

```
Generating an RSA key with a 1024-bit modulus.

You need a user ID for your public key.  The
desired form for this user ID is your name,
followed by your E-mail address enclosed in
<angle brackets>, if you have an E-mail address.
For example:
John Q. Smith <12345.6789@compuserve.com>
Enter a user ID for your public key:
```

At this point, enter your User ID. For our example, we use

```
Dudley Dos <dd@ibm.com>
```

Then, from PGP:

```
You need a pass phrase to protect your RSA
secret key. Your pass phrase can be any sentence
or phrase and may have many words, spaces, punc-
tuation, or any other printable characters.

Enter pass phrase:
```

This is an important step. Any time you use your secret key, PGP needs your passphrase to retrieve it. The passphrase should

be something that is (1) easy to remember so that you don't have
to write it down, but (2) difficult to guess. Finding a passphrase
that meets both criteria isn't as easy as it might sound. I highly
recommend you read through Chapter 13 at some point. For now,
take your best shot; you can always change your passphrase later
without changing your key.

Once you have entered a passphrase, PGP comes back with:

```
We need to generate 1120 random bits.  This is
done by measuring the time intervals between
your keystrokes.  Please enter some random text
on your keyboard until you hear the beep:
```

Type anything you like at a normal pace. PGP uses the timing and the actual characters you enter to generate the random
numbers needed in the key generation process. While you are typing, you see a number on the screen that counts down to 0. PGP
then beeps you and issues the following:

```
   0 *
 -Enough, thank you.
..++++!.............++++!EK

Key generation completed.
```

The series of pluses, dots and other characters are just an indication that PGP is working on the key generation. The characters
have the following interpretations:

  . Number tested is not a prime
  + Number tested may be a prime
  ! Number tested is a prime
  E Trying an exponent
  K Generating components of the key

Some implementations of PGP only display the periods and plus signs.

7.3 SIGNING YOUR KEY

Before doing anything else with PGP, you should sign your public key. Your signature on your key guarantees that no one can tamper with your key or User ID without detection. PGP uses your secret key to sign your public key. The command to issue is of the following form:

```
pgp -ks dd@ibm.com
```

Again, the qualifier k indicates that this is a key management operation; the qualifier s indicates that the requested operation is to sign a key. Finally, the command ends with the User ID or part of the User ID to be signed. In this case, you are signing your own key.

PGP responds:

```
Current time: 1994/08/01 21:26 GMT

A secret key is required to make a signature.
You specified no user ID to select your secret
key, so the default user ID and key will be the
most recently added key on your secret keyring.

Looking for key for user 'dd@ibm.com':

Key for user ID: Dudley Dos <dd@ibm.com>
1024-bit key, Key ID 26F51655, created 1994/08/01

READ CAREFULLY:  Based on your own direct first-
hand knowledge, are you absolutely certain that
you are prepared to solemnly certify that the
above public key actually belongs to the user
specified by the above user ID (y/N)?
```

You may have more than one secret key, in which case you

need to specify which one you want to use. If you don't specify it, PGP picks the most recent such key. PGP shows which key it is going to sign, listing the size of the key, the User ID, and the creation date. It also shows the Key ID, which is a unique numeric identifier for this key.

When you sign a key, yours or someone else's, you are certifying that this key belongs to the person identified by the User ID in question. So, to make sure, PGP asks if you are absolutely certain. If you are certain, you answer PGP's question with a "y" and PGP responds:

```
You need a pass phrase to unlock your RSA secret
key. Key for user ID "Dudley Dos <dd@ibm.com>"

Enter pass phrase:
```

Whenever you sign a message or a public key, PGP must use your secret key, and to get your secret key it needs your passphrase. Enter your passphrase and PGP completes the signing operation:

```
Pass phrase is good.  Just a moment....
Key signature certificate added.
```

7.4 EXTRACTING YOUR KEY

Your correspondents need your public key in order to send you encrypted messages, and to verify your signature on your messages to them. Now that you have signed your key, extract it into a text file, which can then be sent to potential correspondents or posted on a public key server. The command is:

```
pgp -kxa dd@ibm.com mykey
```

This tells PGP to extract (x) a key and store it in a text file (a for
ASCII); the User ID specifies the key to extract and the last parameter, mykey, is the name of the file to be created. PGP responds:

```
Extracting from key ring: 'pubring.pgp', userid
"dd@ibm.com".

Key for user ID: Dudley Dos <dd@ibm.com>
1024-bit key, Key ID 26F51655, created 1994/08/01

Transport armor file: mykey.asc

Key extracted to file 'mykey.asc'.
```

The following is a print-out of the file mykey.asc:

```
-----BEGIN PGP PUBLIC KEY BLOCK-----
Version: 2.7

mQCNAi49aEoAAAEEAKN19RAduc9NONNgVrR+LjbgkTyQNuy0kL7r0CkN2LcSWdmK
+AokJszB11UkhTxPpwDQBNVE1ehDXtkl8Tet6SV2JR1Vn8Bq6bZY8FlzcJaMhIm1
WhhE5guWC0T1ZWoo7ZLLjMev1mEjAHWh6XQYtGy/Xw8gJiBQ3Sz/c2Im9RZVAAUR
tBdEdWRsZXkgRG9zIDxkZEBpYm0uY29tPokAlQIFEC49aHAs/3NiJvUWVQEBYfED
/11T5iPsPdUKnYlipDSkBJXn1lYqmkz1ipO4b+wg3BGjSeTnTvucqTEU++LtTarM
VxgQ75CeqTC6NjQypoQVaZ6zrHdrNRRb7yPiCfDMorqUF/AeOlbw7cEU0aQnEOBx
1q2PRuF71nS6ZVsw2tDvM+JY60tMHH9gFg9WTTJcPeyi
=czoH
-----END PGP PUBLIC KEY BLOCK-----
```

When this file is read by another user's PGP, it can be converted
into the proper format and stored on a public key ring.

7.5 PREPARING A MESSAGE FOR TRANSMISSION

You now have your public and secret keys organized and ready for
use. Before actually exchanging messages with others, let's go

through a little practice session. Fortunately, PGP makes this very easy to do by allowing multiple keys on your secret key ring. You can create a second public/secret key pair with a different User ID. Now you have two "personalities" and the two can exchange messages.

First, issue the command pgp -kg again. Following the steps outlined previously, PGP create a new pair of keys and stores them on your two key rings. To keep things simple, choose a 512-bit key with a User ID of temp and a passphrase of temp. Now, let us prepare a message from you to temp.

As input for this exercise, you can use any file on your system. For example, let us use the file config.txt. It's handy because it is in the pgp directory and it is a text file, so you can compare the input and the output.

Here is the command:

```
pgp -esa config.txt temp -u dd@ibm.com
```

This tells PGP to encrypt (e) and sign (s) the file config.txt and to convert the result to a text (a) format suitable for electronic mailing. The intended recipient is the user temp. The phrase -u dd@ibm.com tells PGP to use the secret key for the user with User ID dd@ibm.com; if there is only one key on your secret key ring, you don't need this qualifier. PGP responds to this command as follows:

```
Current time: 1994/08/01 21:44 GMT

A secret key is required to make a signature.
You need a pass phrase to unlock your RSA secret
key. Key for user ID "Dudley Dos <dd@ibm.com>"

Enter pass phrase:
```

This is the same sequence we saw before for signing a key. The user must respond with the passphrase for this secret key, to which PGP responds:

```
Pass phrase is good.
Key for user ID: Dudley Dos <dd@ibm.com>

1024-bit key, Key ID 26F51655, created 1994/08/01
Just a moment....

Recipients' public key(s) will be used to encrypt.
Key for user ID: temp 512-bit key, Key ID
64E670A5, created 1994/08/01
.
Transport armor file: config.asc
```

This shows that the secret key for Dudley Dos was used to sign the message and that the public key for user temp was used for encrypting the message. The result is stored in the file `config.asc`. Unless told otherwise, PGP always creates a file with the same name as the input file but ending in `.asc`. The result is shown in Figure 7.1.

The result in Figure 7.1 appears to be gibberish and is indecipherable by anyone not in possession of temp's secret key. It has the additional feature that the file consists of nothing but printable characters. The file is formatted such that it can be transmitted through any e-mail system without risk of alteration. There is little danger of a change caused by the e-mail transfer process that would make it impossible to recover the original file. This is why it is referred to as a transport armor file: It is protected from damage during transport.

7.6 PROCESSING A RECEIVED MESSAGE

Once a transport armor file is prepared, it can be sent out as the body of an e-mail message. In fact, if you have a way of sending e-mail to yourself, you should do this. If not, just take the file config.asc and pretend it arrived from an e-mail system. What we want to do now is the reverse of the sending operation, namely, decrypt the file using the receiver's (temp) secret key and then validate the signature using the sender's (Dudley Dos) public key.

Incidentally, if you do send this file to yourself, you are left with an incoming message that includes not only the contents of

```
-----BEGIN PGP MESSAGE-----
Version: 2.7

hEwCFjRyZmTmcKUBAfsELgz1gVxtCK8RP6zzCqAVdOCctNQ7OI3sGiBciQSsdlex
QZWpgf3u4O+kMRay2KIIMyZbFmrOdo4Qefj/jlGupgAACtdi0QVPKUYYw+jhPht5
FFoUk7pYXbiRayB9+e6LMzhrZGe0bvhQbeUGgTm99Gq4JcgBR9T3n0bTQceHiP/E
EPzDo2DUn11JpNbjWELa2VZfCFEntNvUWqsFddWo/FDfITxg7B45ZmDkwjPbTTke
3V6mJt9jx8OwLNQ88h7HRnmHwUiiKLiLp2HNfGPn1eJsDQ7R+wfM9PgzN2OA+Hoq
+S+nXq5V23ILsGEav/NkIEtixFageYYnp/epv9hoEPug96IQNisCAVK8xdGuKD/n
GPpihqLLrZjnFtBTXysOCdYVRI3y9d/PL326bVWpLN2hHtUEBuoyhg0DbYQxGHNZ
bgffmSTBAzFzTovK1jKaUF+dUE5UVcskRkZsYHKAYcL/s2VWL7eroJHNiF+dmDkZ
y1I+/WMNt059kQ3YnG5m730pUCuc22ZA6mSRGBloI6vP8PDNsfxWU+oXMPIg1LLp
9PJOJvqAsTehhaW0qqRgWGco7hCvF+n71RTHrAwllcj6c+WVAOMGBG3Qvbe4vhZG
9hVWm47NQEBdem+upjDiUHcqsHFxf269IXJwhPrhVYJr80UVqVgRwKYI2u5y8mkR
xzAH3SVRiLvA61o/ZmCnDlsypApiopd4kcArlpg/+RP3Yv24vXfp2pk807bNsT18
DjSmw+SV+iVigekMCUitinuOdFez9zZ6cgIwZITWruihRwYDz+JDJdcxcVQbrnZd
8W1QQDAYQpxQq7HHbbSb6eI/pz72/qEp6cDRQfogmCICORnjnnkoZ/tJ6L1XnZOA
nvVPQL01IQi+m0gI+TbDObHqIz52drJ6irsZtpOi8KfsP+MTDTtIdQbnppJo4pN1
C4q8ZvvwoTx3UYj5Jsy02712tkB0+fFjpKEwYTq9GS3cmMhLRqvuoDDqRTLt5L/u
nOdPvJgd9h9fZ0cLF9C9Dh28NvR1T8nWAT/wCXXEDStNnc7buIM9dzOtCaTXYm3r
72O76/6/up5yOETV39hZOVTpXDXS10JVWKSB04t6XPUCBZbZVlHZy0qaaiDR58RA
25G3/f3wVwxkl/tDTBr2NyY4KOzgkFtKrb7D2179oDewcgFxEzi2xkPLFWqqWPep
2izhQYMG6hRgBsEWlfL03JXju+QCcFjlnZZu/1aqwcuEyX31kVym4cjiZ0GFdcxn
KDo8PzAgE3J0bfBL+YZDnd+Y2FeQkCdrer2J0cPvc0V8VX8JstUtyBr8IsrBkp8P
wW30bKaMu9JT8+bm9BvqPxKTROYhb2n189QARtG2LhxUviHvP1fLJpF+h+MAsEm5
+ufn8TZ4oP34PuOskzc9FbRpuHtg1ojWXWkh4UbXLCVv9t3DzS48hMSgRdD2TWeO
hK9AiicYH2XMl3+PHwZFajIqcGAYIWr+17VM3qD1SYZKTZOIu46TeBtYA82d7IpT
869HFob5473F3HcG2oTHSAnAyhuq+XpTJJu/xuwiCCrPctDptGqUSLvrj3Rpkr4n
99kpWoeXufPv3X51c+NyG9+YB4tkr0UHDAwEdRjjqbDSHkphoGkVS1zipBl+hJdj
8nqFIR3om9ryNly2Ca/GMrMif78B6ATPMWLhPb47OV560I/3Sxftv6osujTwNvpP
xJgA90Xu0ctBtcmjFU+UDZ/wHU4zy7lqZaK8FBKVmbaQ2+tOlH5jjI+fu5Ebfy1t
N1cfbLrNqRttDozNTwx5rzWnYZ6GEI2jvby1SmIYGnh/GHSCgJDptEfV+y7psj3z
wQOEo5trreZaKfYsd2zbic7omKcuwOq73tj8HXz7MZ4Z8yq5EwZtYpRtWrQDFxoY
+T31w/Gdj3tqLKUt8ndWSeWJosF9/UNYDATuR7P5dL0/tvDFJVAGkDFHUf9jG4Ph
Swrj3YnKMObtks61AjiAoVVXmYRKImsqErXqVH5ztFfuM6gyyp1OM1IQRo+HfpAP
7Iud6/HsyDD9UNZY2+zZiMojqa+lLM7iWbZ3onYAlNpbvA0kvM6Cha2Jj1qUmV7s
dCEKc8h3ha2Q0OrNJQHJKwjSpKJVdCE1Hx232FeJs6eYnynZhkzGYc+Poqn6IW7G
```

(continued)

Fig **7.1** Encrypted, Signed Copy of config.txt

```
iZuNPpggRpZv+GseonlvvSbPCJ6k3JDuK4zWZYJfXgdm7oJShfhQW463TaL0vulQ
b4dA+KAys2tpvdSrxAdTFWyeVy6FqDt6A7IZXedIzLbmAi4puwPwfazguufDxL0R
T/1YAyiA8TDyFJEL5ZP9yngZJa84HAk87BxyD9xNIt1M4FBvWENsN2m4ylSQPL55
orZRwg6TZKegF8za+WiDqU+NryQUfvU17zOKrY+jHOBIqQtW9ObS7XNINz5P8ff6
RgaCNcHY4woz4Qrvcv0OvSeZ0O51LBHbOQ4e0omHDSTa+2xhL44h1zbON/M1bu51
KstWUNYcNBag8IhR97Ndqd+I0uX/Df1GtSAcGi1wUgvyAUGRH0TcApyXPJwEv5/a
aX1GXA9iDbss06jyqL/wQiIIIPBUoX4141s/D8pmNdpXhtjAKO4sYyuOckvy/CRK
8YXILCyjtnyPjh5ylp90RhLbmvKy/eympsuludHDG/zdYOjEGfIpPttb4ct6wLiF
xd+OtSUvVK8ow7FFkIttdws24Kp9oXb2duBb7ULtqLaan1Vhh4Pg5U03YAj2Rpna
6/TjXYK6T4QLkmTncCz4jcxbSS/C39SvFy5edC1DEkOW52U8O48rc3Hm0xSFUfvB
GZQStWV/XbTkRsshfm7QCz01R6gZ+1s4yFxLcC20kL+oNihz4tReBk8+0hP3q9QX
GzTgFDVKqjRyrlhITiwU3HNnWRQMFjAXtUoudZis27U5P9kpiT1rSRzya8gd+Xum
eMPTcyTxXqBBwPwFdhG7WDI8vYIdBOJQ/EKuv6D3D/ejJp0gD9Z7C5HaMyuHTdD2
PtT8J8juhHsmMTFYeiSa2x1pM7S4ICiUDkvSv3DLGuKF6rHTvk9/6zBRxRY6zPUm
3ecSiNkvJfN9948XSJD2VDKeHRVau7owhcG5IgnoLEDnZeMQMMNSLwV5dYmXVYBL
5WzYm/ii4io2aQ7+2PdS2FNd8PMnMZmEURtk13B5Bu5XVgLIJEcnAtfNwhtYt8jL
NHjCz4K0614g1QORBa3SpDqTYxSy2PnZ5TtQ3UQpg0TiPwZDAJC7G4++oDGNjwJc
xCCiD13CHnC+UgraY/0eqoOALZ4yuXKU2J2BS92VocaieJNqO9QAqwnjU5cVw5t8
NqUx4gKBMsFNZt/LPVaHvtc1W6rn7MHbByh3QWwmCAouin5/C0Qf1yNBQf6mzW8E
Dq0/WQy/IVHVT/kFoLYCshDKeFQhJE6ukVH1DqT4yn1Pk7fdECOBNsbip7eoCkny
P9ABGSOTiEowPvGtgGHiZ2alf+bVY3ivUpqv5A2t/5mbu28yfcTC5nR29dXrQRIS
OkMzzxi0YesYnLaR1AguFGWjh3bnM6/aAHzQCzosGuo4UeUTR/jhCqJpD26qBFpM
gfkhGf5puC3ZwCyyq7Df1GgJV/AtHJb2KGli/Y4nc1Iot97ncFu04r9rvv9vn4UR
G5YRViJ7giGu4ejyozpDD6Tvzuo6tps7EN4BSWdIVsZZJAv5oric8CZnqyFdlv1i
F7arPTRZUslcwfqFYvbZKW7xkKN3bvuj/o3VyBmQs4+R1NR+oOWIPwpJUFDL3hLx
Tp7mO2O69N1xlmkWtKHnSVQinSwcBxtV/30=
=Bhpv
-----END PGP MESSAGE-----
```

Fig **7.1**   Encrypted, Signed Copy of config.txt *(continued)*

Figure 7.1 but also some header lines that indicate the sender, receiver, and subject of the message. No matter. PGP ignores anything that isn't enclosed between the lines:

        -----BEGIN PGP MESSAGE-----

and

        -----END PGP MESSAGE-----

So, we assume that temp has just received a message, which has been stored under the file name config.asc, and wishes to recover a readable copy. The command is:

```
pgp config.asc
```

This tells PGP to take the file indicated and (1) decrypt it if it is encrypted and (2) check the signature if it is signed. We don't have to tell PGP which keys to use because the Key IDs of the keys involved accompany the message. In particular, temp's secret key is used in the decryption process and Dudley's public key is used in the signature verification process.

PGP's response to the command is:

```
File is encrypted.  Secret key is required to read it.
Key for user ID: temp

512-bit key, Key ID 64E670A5, created 1994/08/01
You need a pass phrase to unlock your RSA secret key.
Enter pass phrase:
```

The first thing PGP does is the decryption, and for this it needs temp's secret key. To get that key, PGP requires temp's passphrase. After temp enters the passphrase, PGP responds:

```
Pass phrase is good.  Just a moment......
File has signature.  Public key is required to check
signature.
Good signature from user "Dudley Dos <dd@ibm.com>".
Signature made 1994/08/01 21:44 GMT

Plaintext filename: config
```

The resulting output is stored in file config. If you check this against the original input from config.txt, the two should be identical.

7.7 ADDING KEYS TO YOUR PUBLIC KEY RING

Now that you have seen that PGP works, it is time to add some public keys to your key ring so that you can correspond with others. First, we might as well dispense with the temp key. To remove it from your secret ring, type:

```
pgp -kr temp secring.pgp
```

This is a key management command (k) to remove (r) the key with User ID temp from the key ring secring.pgp. PGP's response is:

```
Removing from key ring: 'secring.pgp', userid "temp".
Key for user ID: temp
512-bit key, Key ID 64E670A5, created 1994/08/01
Are you sure you want this key removed (y/N)?
```

Respond with a "y", and PGP deletes the key and reports:

```
Key removed from key ring.
```

You can remove the public key for temp from pubring.pgp with a similar dialog. Now we are ready to add some "real" keys to your public key ring. A good place to start is the set of keys that come with the implementation. These are generally to be found in a file with the name keys.asc. The contents of this file depend on the implementation. For example, PGP 2.6 and MacPGP 2.6 include a set of keys for the developers, many of whom are from MIT. In this section, we are using ViaCrypt PGP 2.7, so we would expect a ViaCrypt key. In any case, the command for adding all of these keys to your public key ring is:

```
pgp -ka keys.asc
```

This is a key management command (k) to add (a) keys to your
public key ring from the file keys.asc. PGP's response is:

```
Looking for new keys...
pub     1024/C7A966DD     1993/05/21     Philip R. Zimmermann
                                         <prz@acm.org>
pub     512/67ECF13D      1993/07/29     David A. Barnhart
                                         <CIS:70275,1360>
pub     1024/CB768501     1993/10/13     ViaCrypt <Phone (602) 944-0773>

Checking signatures...
pub     1024/C7A966DD     1993/05/21     Philip R. Zimmermann
                                         <prz@acm.org>
sig!         67ECF13D     1993/07/30     David A. Barnhart
                                         <CIS:70275,1360>
pub     512/67ECF13D      1993/07/29     David A. Barnhart
                                         <CIS:70275,1360>
sig!         C7A966DD     1993/10/25     Philip R. Zimmermann
                                         <prz@acm.org>
sig!         CB768501     1993/10/25     ViaCrypt <Phone (602) 944-0773>
pub     1024/CB768501     1993/10/13     ViaCrypt <Phone (602) 944-0773>
sig!         C7A966DD     1993/10/25     Philip R. Zimmermann
                                         <prz@acm.org>
sig!         CB768501     1993/10/25     ViaCrypt <Phone (602) 944-0773>

Keyfile contains:
   3 new key(s)


One or more of the new keys are not fully certified.
Do you want to certify any of these keys yourself (y/N)?
```

This shows that three new keys have been added to your public
key ring. David Barnhart is the PGP product manager at
ViaCrypt, and there is a generic ViaCrypt key. PGP also shows the
signatures that are attached to each of these public keys. The presence of a signature means that the signer is certifying that the
signed key is valid; that is, the key is owned by the person identi-

fied by the associated User ID.

After listing the keys that have been entered, PGP alerts the user that one or more of the keys are not fully certified. For a key to be fully certified, it must be signed by you or by someone you have designated to be trusted to sign keys. So far, you have not granted such trust to anyone, so the keys remain uncertified. For now, answer "N" to this question.

Let's see how we have done, by viewing the current contents of your public key ring:

```
pgp -kv
```

This is a key management command (k) to view (v) the public key ring. We get:

```
Key ring: 'pubring.pgp'
Type   bits/keyID    Date         User ID
pub    1024/C7A966DD 1993/05/21   Philip R. Zimmermann <prz@acm.org>
pub     512/67ECF13D 1993/07/29   David A. Barnhart
                                  <CIS:70275,1360>
pub    1024/CB768501 1993/10/13   ViaCrypt <Phone  (602) 944-0773>
                                  ViaCrypt <70304.41@compuserve.com>
                                  ViaCrypt <viacrypt@acm.org>
                                  ViaCrypt <FAX (602) 943-2601>
pub    1024/26F51655 1994/08/01   Dudley Dos <dd@ibm.com>
4 matching keys found.
```

There are four keys, including the user's. Note that the ViaCrypt key includes four separate User IDs; nevertheless, it is a single public key. If you want to see the signatures, you need to issue the same command in verbose (v) mode:

```
pgp -kvv
```

Then you get:

```
Key ring: 'pubring.pgp'
  Type  bits/keyID      Date          User ID
  pub   1024/C7A966DD   1993/05/21    Philip R. Zimmermann
                                      <prz@acm.org>
  sig         67ECF13D                David A. Barnhart
                                      <CIS:70275,1360>
  sig         8DE722D9                (Unknown signator, can't be
                                      checked)
  sig         865AA7F3                (Unknown signator, can't be
                                      checked)
  sig         FF67F70B                (Unknown signator, can't be
                                      checked)
  pub   512/67ECF13D    1993/07/29    David A. Barnhart <CIS:70275,1360>
  sig         C7A966DD                Philip R.    Zimmermann
                                      <prz@acm.org>
  sig         CB768501                ViaCrypt <Phone (602) 944-0773>
  pub   1024/CB768501   1993/10/13    ViaCrypt <Phone (602) 944-0773>
  sig         C7A966DD                Philip R. Zimmermann <prz@acm.org>
  sig         CB768501                ViaCrypt <Phone (602) 944-0773>
                                      ViaCrypt <70304.41@compuserve.com>
                                      ViaCrypt <viacrypt@acm.org>
                                      ViaCrypt <FAX (602) 943-2601>
  pub   1024/26F51655   1994/08/01    Dudley Dos <dd@ibm.com>
  sig         26F51655                Dudley Dos <dd@ibm.com>
4 matching keys found.
```

Here we see that Phil Zimmermann's key has been signed by "unknown signators." This simply means that you have no key on this ring for the Key ID associated with this signature.

7.8 VERIFYING PGP

So far, you have only been playing around with PGP on your own system. Before making serious use of PGP, you should verify that your version hasn't been tampered with in any way. It is conceivable that someone has introduced a virus that could damage your computer files or some sort of "back door" that allows them to defeat PGP's security. What you can do is use the power of PGP to check your copy of PGP.

Every implementation of PGP comes with a signature of one of the developers. When PGP is shipped or posted to an ftp site, the developer signs the executable module of PGP. The signature is stored separately in a file with a name such as `pgpsig.asc`. Just as you can verify the signature of a message, you can verify the signature of your PGP execution module. If the signature is valid, this proves that your copy of PGP is from the genuine source and hasn't been altered.

There is a bit of a circular problem here: The executable file is signed with a developer's secret key (in this case ViaCrypt) and you have obtained the developer's public key from the file `keys.asc` that came with PGP! So first you must somehow verify the developer's key. There are a number of ways of doing this, discussed in Chapter 6. One of the most efficient is by means of a key fingerprint. If you enter the command:

```
pgp -kvc viacrypt
```

PGP checks (c) the public key of User ID viacrypt and displays:

```
Key ring: c:\pgp\pubring.pgp', looking for user ID ''viacrypt''.
Type        bits/keyID        Date      User ID
pub    1024/CB768501     1993/10/13     ViaCrypt <Phone (602) 944-0773>
Key fingerprint = EC A9 0D F1 87 F7 8A 75  91 3B 1C 6A 8B 9A 8B 2F
                                           ViaCrypt <70304.41@compuserve.com>
                                           ViaCrypt <viacrypt@acm.org>
                                           ViaCrypt <FAX (602) 943-2601>
1 matching key found.
```

A key fingerprint is simply a string of 32 hexadecimal digits that is, for all practical purposes, unique to a particular key (which is why it is called a fingerprint). The fingerprint that PGP displays is generated from the key that is actually on your public key ring. Now all you have to do is verify that key. To do this, you need to get the fingerprint from a separate source. In the case of ViaCrypt, you can verify the fingerprint by calling ViaCrypt's customer support department and having them dictate the fingerprint to you over the phone. For other implementations, you may be able to use the telephone technique, either directly to the developer or to someone else that you trust. Otherwise, you may have to get another copy of the developer's key from a different source, such as a key server.

Once you have verified the developer's key, you can verify PGP. Simply enter:

```
pgp pgpsig.asc
```

Recall that this tells PGP to take the file indicated and (1) decrypt it if it is encrypted and (2) check the signature if it is signed. PGP responds:

```
File has signature.  Public key is required to check signature.
File 'pgpsig.$00' has signature, but with no text.
Please enter filename of material that signature applies to:
```

PGP discovers that the file contains a signature but that the signed material isn't present. It therefore asks the user where to find the file that is signed with this signature. The user responds with the file name pgp.exe. Then PGP responds:

```
Good signature from user ''ViaCrypt <Phone (602) 944-0773>''.
Signature made 1994/06/21 20:23 GMT

WARNING: Because this public key is not certified with a
trusted signature, it is not known with high confidence that
this public key actually belongs to: ''ViaCrypt <Phone (602)
944-0773>''.

Signature and text are separate. No output file produced.
```

This assures you that your copy of PGP has not been tampered with. Note the warning: Although ViaCrypt's key is on your public key ring, you have not certified it to be valid. Therefore, PGP

checks the signature on pgp.exe but warns you that it is not sure
of the validity of ViaCrypt's public key. Since you are now sure of
the key's validity, you should sign it. Enter:

```
pgp -ks viacrypt
```

   And get back:

```
A secret key is required to make a signature.
You specified no user ID to select your secret key,so
the default user ID and key will be the most recently
added key on your secret keyring.

Looking for key for user 'viacrypt':

Key for user ID: ViaCrypt <Phone (602) 944-0773>
1024-bit key, Key ID CB768501, created 1993/10/13
Also known as: ViaCrypt <70304.41@compuserve.com>
Also known as: ViaCrypt <viacrypt@acm.org>
Also known as: ViaCrypt <FAX (602) 943-2601>

READ CAREFULLY:  Based on your own direct first-hand
knowledge, are you absolutely certain that you are
prepared to solemnly certify that the above public key
actually belongs to the user specified by the above
user ID (y/N)?
```

If you answer yes, PGP prompts you for your passphrase in order
to sign the ViaCrypt key. PGP then displays:

```
Key signature certificate added.

Make a determination in your own mind whether this key
actually belongs to the person whom you think it be
longs to, based on available evidence. If you think it
                                          (continued)
```

```
does, then based on your estimate of that person's
integrity and competence in key management, answer the
following question:
Would you trust ''ViaCrypt <Phone (602) 944-0773>''
to act as an introducer and certify other people's pub-
lic keys to you?
(1=I don't know. 2=No. 3=Usually. 4=Yes, always.) ?
```

Once you have certified that the key is valid by signing it, PGP asks you whether or not you trust the owner of this key to certify other keys. If so, answer with a "4." Now, if you obtain any other key signed by ViaCrypt, PGP automatically adds it to your key ring as a valid key.

DOS PGP
Reference

T his chapter summarizes the
commands used in the DOS and UNIX versions of PGP. A final section discusses the use of a DOS shell to simplify the user interface.

All commands in DOS PGP are entered at the DOS prompt
with a line beginning with pgp, and are of the form:

```
pgp -options  parameters
```

The first phrase after pgp begins with a dash and is followed by a
sequence of one or more letters. Each letter represents a command
option. At least one option must be selected, except in the case of
file decryption. Following the options phrase is a sequence of zero
or more parameters. Possible parameters include file names, User
IDs, and key rings.

8.1 MESSAGE/FILE PROCESSING

Encryption and Signature Operations

Table 8.1 shows the most common commands for processing
files or messages.[1] The most common commands have to do with
encrypting and signing a plaintext file. The simplest forms of these
commands do the following:

---

[1] In all of the tables in this chapter, an item enclosed in square brackets is optional;
if the optional parameter is not present, PGP selects the appropriate default. An
italicized item represents a variable name rather than a true value.

- Encrypt: The file *filename* is encrypted using the public key[2] indicated by *her-userid*.
- Sign: The file *filename* is signed using this user's secret key. If the user has more than one secret key, the user may specify which one, with a parameter signaled by -u; otherwise, PGP uses the first key on the user's `secring.pgp`.
- Sign and Encrypt: Both of the preceding two operations are performed.

USER ID OR KEY ID SELECTION

Many of the commands listed in the tables indicate the selection of a key on the basis of User ID. It isn't necessary to enter the entire User ID. If a partial User ID is entered, PGP will do a search to match that string. For example, in Dudley Dos's key ring (Chapter 7), the string prz will select Phil Zimmermann's key.

In addition, anywhere in the tables that it is indicated that a key can be selected on the basis of User ID, it can also be selected on the basis of Key ID. The convention is to enter a zero followed by the letter x followed by part or all of the Key ID. For example, the string 0x7A9 will select Phil Zimmermann's key.

Two command options may be included in any of the preceding three commands. The -a option causes PGP to convert the output to ASCII armor format, so that the output can be sent via electronic mail. Without this option, part or all of the output will be raw binary data and may be corrupted or rejected by an e-mail facility. The -t option tells PGP to treat the input as an ASCII text file. When this option is present, PGP first converts the input to canonical form. Later, when the message is received on another system and the original file is recovered, PGP converts from *canonical form* to the local text format. Primarily, these conversions have to do with the proper handling of carriage returns and line feeds, as explained in Chapter 4.

---

[2] The actual procedure is to use conventional encryption with a one-time session key and then to encrypt that session key with the recipient's public key and attach the result to the ciphertext; for convenience we simply say that the plaintext is encrypted using the recipient's public key.

Table **8.1**

PGP Message/File Processing Commands

Function	Command
encrypt a plaintext file with the recipient's public key	pgp -e *filename her_userid*
sign a plaintext file with your secret key	pgp -s *filename* [-u *your_userid]*
sign a plaintext file with your secret key, and then encrypt it with the recipient's public key	pgp -es *filename her_userid* [-u *your_userid*]
sign a plaintext file with your secret key, then encrypt it with the recipient's public key, and produce ASCII armor output	pgp -esa *filename her_userid* [-u *your_userid*]
sign a plaintext ASCII text file with your secret key, and then encrypt it with the recipient's public key	pgp -est *filename her_userid* [-u *your_userid*]
sign a plaintext ASCII text file with your secret key, then encrypt it with the recipient's public key, and produce ASCII armor output	pgp -esta *filename her_userid* [-u *your_userid*]
encrypt a message for any number of recipients	pgp -e *filename userid1 userid2 userid3*
encrypt a plaintext file with just conventional cryptography	pgp -c *filename*
decrypt an encrypted file, or check the signature integrity of a signed file	pgp *ciphertextfilename*.pgp [-o *plaintextfilename*]
create an ASCII-armored file, without signing and without encrypting	pgp -a *filename*

TIP: USING PGP TO PROTECT FILES

If you issue the command:

pgp -a *filename*

PGP will produce a file, *filename*.asc, with ASCII armor but without a signature and without encryption. Thus PGP provides a handy way of

protecting a binary file for e-mail transmission even though security services aren't needed. Anyone with PGP will be able to de-armor it without difficulty by issuing pgp *filename*.asc. In addition, for long files, the
-a command conveniently produces a multi-part file for transmission.

The file can also be compressed, as long as you perform some other
PGP function at the same time. For instance, you can sign the file:

pgp -sa *filename*

The -a and -t options can be used separately or together and
can be added to the -e, -s, and -es commands, for a total of 12 different variations on these basic commands (-e, -s, -es, -ea, -sa, -esa,
-et, -st, -est, -eta, -sta, -esta).

When one of the preceding commands without -a is executed,
PGP produces a file that ends in .pgp. If the input file ends in .pgp,
PGP asks the user whether to overwrite the file or to use a new file
name. When one of the preceding commands with -a is executed,
PGP produces a file that ends in .asc. If the input file happens to
end in .asc, then PGP will overwrite that file. Careful!

Any of the commands that involve encryption (-e, -es, -ea, -
esa, -et, -est, -eat, -esta) can be encrypted for multiple recipients
by listing the User ID of each recipient. Only one output file is created, and this can be sent to each recipient.

CLEAR SIGNING A FILE

For some PGP implementations, the default clearsig value is on,
whereas for others the default value is off. If the current setting of
the clearsig parameter is on, then to clear sign a file, use the following command:

pgp -sta filename

The resulting text file can be displayed without using PGP and can
therefore be read by anyone. However, the message is signed, assuring its authenticity.

If the current setting of the clearsig parameter is off, then use the following command to clear sign a file:

pgp -sta +clearsig=on filename

Note that you must always use both the -t and the -a command options.

Finally, you can encrypt a file using only conventional encryption with the -c option. In this case, PGP prompts you for a one-time passphrase and use that passphrase to generate the encryption key. Later, to decrypt the file enter the usual decryption command; PGP prompts you for the passphrase.

TIP: ENCRYPTING A BATCH OF FILES

To encrypt a set of files in a subdirectory, the DOS FOR command can be used. For example, if you have a number of text files ending in .txt, then use the following command:

FOR %f in (*.txt) DO pgp -cw %f

PGP will prompt you one file at a time for a passphrase. When the operation is complete, all of the .txt files will have been replaced with encrypted .pgp files. To decrypt all of these files at once do:

FOR %f in (*.pgp) DO pgp %f

For these procedures, the directory should be the current working directory. Also, there should be no subdirectories below the one in use that have a name ending in .txt.

If you have many files to encrypt, the repeated prompts for a passphrase become tedious. As an alternative, you can use ZIP or some other compression program to compress a number of files into one archive file. You can then encrypt the archive file.

Decryption and Signature Verification

Processing an incoming file doesn't require the listing of any command options. PGP checks to see if the file is encrypted. If it is, PGP decrypts it using the recipient's secret key. Next, PGP checks to see if the file is signed. If so, PGP checks the signature using the sender's public key and then removes the signature.

If the file is encrypted, it includes the Key ID of the public key that was used in the encryption process. PGP searches the user's secring.pgp for the matching secret key. If that key isn't present, PGP prints out a warning message. If the file is signed, it includes the Key ID of the public key of the signer. PGP searches the user's pubring.pgp for the public key. If that key isn't present, PGP prints out a warning.

When PGP prepares a message with ASCII armor, if the size of the output exceeds the limit specified in the configuration parameter ArmorLines (see Section 8.4), then PGP produces a sequence of output files labeled .as1, .as2, and so on. When the recipient issues the command PGP *file*.as1, PGP automatically looks for *file*.as2, *file*.as3, etc.

The output from the decryption and/or signature processing is stored in a new file with the following naming conventions. If the old file ends in .asc or .pgp, then the new file has the same name without the .asc or .pgp. Otherwise, the new file has the same name as the old file and PGP asks whether you want to overwrite. You can specify the name of the output file up front with the [-o *filename*] parameter.

8.2 KEY MANAGEMENT

All key management commands begin with the -k command option (Table 8.2). For most commands, the default key ring is pubring.pgp, which can be overridden by the use of the [*keyring*] option.

Adding, Copying, and Removing Keys

To generate a new key pair, use the -kg command option. PGP places a new secret key on secring.pgp and the matching public key on pubring.pgp. You may have multiple secret keys on secring.pgp, so long as each one has a unique User ID.

An undocumented feature, available on most DOS implementation, enables you to specify key size and exponent size. For example, if you enter

```
pgp -kg 1024
```

then PGP generates a new key pair with a 1024-bit key size. This saves the step in which PGP prompts you for a key size. If you enter

```
pgp -kg 1024 128
```

Table **8.2**

PGP Key Management Commands

Function	Command
generate your own unique public/secret key pair	pgp -kg [*keysize*] [*expsize*]
extract (copy) a key from a public or secret key ring	pgp -kx *userid keyfile* [*keyring*] or pgp -kxa *userid keyfile* [*keyring*]
add a public or secret key file's contents to a public or secret key ring	pgp -ka *keyfile* [*keyring*]
remove a key or just a userid from a public key ring	pgp -kr *userid* [*keyring*]
remove selected signatures from a userid on a keyring	pgp -krs *userid* [*keyring*]
view the keys on a key ring	pgp -kv [*userid*] [*keyring*]
view the keys and signatures on a key ring	pgp -kvv [*userid*] [*keyring*]
view the keys, signatures, and trust levels on a public key ring	pgp -kc [*userid*] [*keyring*]
search for ultimately trusted keys and display a signature chain starting from these keys	pgp -km [*keyring*]
view the "fingerprint" of a public key	pgp -kvc [*userid*] [*keyring*]
add a new userid to your public key or change the pass phrase for your secret key	pgp -ke [*userid*] [*keyring*]
edit the trust parameters for a public key	pgp -ke [*userid*] [*keyring*]
sign and certify a public key on your public key ring	pgp -ks *userid* [-u *your_userid*] [*keyring*]
permanently revoke your own key, creating a key compromise certificate	pgp -kd *your_userid*
disable or reenable a public key on your own public key ring	pgp -kd *userid*

PGP generates a new key pair with a 1024-bit key size and a 128-bit public key exponent size. See Chapter 5 for a discussion of public key exponent size.

To make a copy of a key on a key ring, use the -kx or -kxa command. PGP copies the key specified by *userid* and all of its signatures into *keyfile*. You should always use the -a option, which puts the file in ASCII armor format, so that the result can be sent to others via e-mail.

To copy all of the keys on a key ring into a file, use the command

```
pgp -kxa * keyfile [keyring]
```

This produces an ASCII armor file with all of the keys on the designated key ring.

You can add a key that has previously been extracted into a key file (by you or someone else) to your public or secret key ring with the -ka option. If you add a key that already exists, and the keyfile copy contains new User IDs or new signatures, then those new User IDs or signatures are added to the existing key on the key ring.

When you attempt to remove a key with the -kr command, PGP prompts you to make sure you want to remove the key of *userid*. If the key has more than one ID, you are asked if you want to remove the whole key. If not, PGP asks you about each User ID separately. If you remove your own key from the public key ring, PGP asks you whether you also want to remove the matching secret key.

You can use the -krs command to get rid of unknown or unwanted signatures, in order to clean up your public key ring. PGP prompts you one signature at a time for removal.

Viewing Keys

The -kv command provides a concise listing of a key ring or a single key. A single key is listed if the *userid* parameter is included in the command. The concise listing shows the key length in bits, the Key ID, the date of creation, and the User ID or IDs for each key.

TIP: VIEWING OTHER KEY RINGS

The -kv command has some interesting quirks, summarized below:

Command	Effect
pgp -kv	View all keys on default public key ring
pgp -kv *userid*	View all keys on default public key ring with a match to *userid*
pgp -kv *userid keyring*	View all keys on *keyring* with a match to *userid*
pgp -kv *keyring*	View all keys on *keyring* (assuming file name of key ring ends in .pgp)
pgp -kv * *keyring*	View all keys on *keyring*

It appears, according to the manual, that you can examine all the keys in a particular keyring with the command pgp -kv *keyring*. If the file name of the key ring ends in .pgp (e.g. secring.pgp) then the command works as expected. However, if the file name does not end in .pgp (e.g., pubring.bak), PGP interprets this as a command to view User ID keyring on pubring.pgp. To get around this, use the command pgp -kv * *keyring*. The * acts as a wild card indicating all User IDs. This technique also works with -kvv, -kvc, and -kc commands.

The -kvv command provides a more verbose listing of a key ring or single key. In this case PGP also shows the Key ID and User ID of each signature attached to each of the User IDs for each key.

The most verbose listing is provide by the -kc command. Two listings are produced. First, PGP lists the selected key or entire ring, showing all signatures. Then, PGP repeats the listing, this time showing the trust level of each User ID (both for keys and for signatures) and the validity of each key. In fact, PGP is doing more than just displaying this information. The -kc command causes PGP to do a complete pass through your public key ring. Each signature is checked to see if the signer's key is on the ring and if so, the OwnerTrust value assigned to the key owner is copied into the SigTrust value for the corresponding signature. Then, PGP recalculates the Validity for each key. In addition, if the user has defined a backup secret key ring in the config.txt file (see Section 8.4), then PGP checks the user's public key against the secret key on the backup file.

An undocumented feature, available on most DOS implementations, is the -km command option. When this command is executed, PGP displays each key on the public key ring that is ultimately trusted (each of your public keys) and a signature chain for each of these keys. That is, PGP shows which keys are signed by the ultimately trusted key, and then which keys are signed by the keys signed by the ultimately trusted key, and so on.

Finally, the -kvc command displays the fingerprint of the selected key or all of the keys on the key ring.

Editing Keys

The only edit command in PGP is the -ke command. Its interpretation depends on the *userid* parameter.

If there is no *userid*, by default the user's primary public key (the first or only public key for this user on the public key ring), is selected. If there is no *userid*, or if the *userid* refers to one of this user's public keys, then the user is prompted to add a new User ID to this key; the old User ID is retained. Then the user is prompted to change the passphrase for the corresponding secret key.

If the *userid* refers to another public key on the key ring, then the user is prompted to select a trust level for the owner of this key.

Signing, Revoking, and Disabling Keys

You can sign the Key-ID/User-ID combination of any key on a public key ring using the -ks command. The *userid* parameter specifies the key to be signed and can refer to your public key or any other public key on the key ring. If you have more than one secret key, you need to specify which key you will use with the [-u *your_userid*] parameter.

To revoke your own key permanently, use the -kd command. Your public key remains in your public key ring, but is designated as revoked. Extract the revoked key (with the -kxa command) to create a revocation certificate that can be sent to others.

The same -kd command is used to disable another public key temporarily. The key remains on the ring but cannot be used in encrypting messages. At a later time, the -kd command can be used to reenable the key.

Table **8.3**

Other PGP Commands

Function	Command
decrypt a message and leave the signature on it intact	pgp -d *ciphertextfile*
create a signature certificate that is detached from the document	pgp -sb *file* [-u *your_userid*]
detach a signature certificate from a signed message	pgp -b *signedfile*
strip the ASCII armor from a file but do not perform decryption	pgp -da *ciphertextfile*.asc
list all documented PGP commands	pgp -h
list all documented PGP key management functions	pgp -k

8.3 MISCELLANEOUS COMMANDS AND OPTIONS

Signature-Related Commands

Table 8.3 lists several additional signature-related commands. The -d command allows you to decrypt a message but leave the signature attached to it. This enables you or anyone else to determine the validity of the file at a later time.

If you need to create a signature that is separate from the file it signs, use the -sb command. The result is a signature in a file with the same base name as the signed file, but ending in .sig.

If you have a file that includes an attached signature, the -b command creates two new files; one consists of the plaintext without the signature and the other consists of the detached signature. The detached signature will be in a file of the form *filename*.sig.

To verify a detached signature, enter the command pgp *filename*.sig. PGP searches for the file filename; if it doesn't exist, PGP prompts you for the name of the signed file. Then PGP veri-

Table **8.4**

PGP Command Options

Function	Commands
To produce a ciphertext file in ASCII radix-64 format, add the -a option when encrypting or signing a message or extracting a key	pgp -sea *textfile her_userid* or pgp -kxa *userid keyfile* [*keyring*]
To wipe out the plaintext file after producing the ciphertext file, add the -w (wipe) option when encrypting or signing a message	pgp -sew *message.txt her_userid*
To specify that a plaintext file contains ASCII text, not binary, and should be converted to recipient's local text conventions, add the -t (text) option to other options	pgp -seat *message.txt her_userid*
To view the decrypted plaintext output on your screen (like the Unix-style "more" command), without writing it to a file, use the -m (more) option while decrypting	pgp -m *ciphertextfile*
To specify that the recipient's decrypted plaintext will be shown ONLY on her screen and cannot be saved to disk, add the -m option	pgp -steam *message.txt her_userid*
To recover the original plaintext filename while decrypting, add the -p option	pgp -p *ciphertextfile*
To enter your passphrase at the command line rather than waiting for a prompt	pgp -s *textfile* -z *"passphrase" or* pgp *ciphertextfile* -z *"passphrase"*
To use a Unix-style filter mode, reading from standard input and writing to standard output, add the -f option	pgp -feast *her_userid* <*inputfile* >*outputfile*
The -l option provides debug-related information	pgp -kvl

fies the signature. To avoid the prompt, if the detached signature is in file1.sig and the signed file is in file2, then enter

```
pgp file1.sig file2
```

Other Commands

Table 8.3 also lists some other miscellaneous PGP commands. The -da command is useful when you receive an ASCII armor file by e-mail and wish to save the encrypted form of the message. With this command, the ASCII armor is stripped off and the smaller .pgp file is stored, saving disk space.

The -h and -k commands display summaries of documented PGP commands and PGP key management commands, respectively.

Auxiliary Command Options

Table 8.4 lists command options that can be used in combination with other options. Most of these have already been discussed or are self-explanatory. A few warrant some elaboration.

If a message is encrypted and/or signed with the -m option, then PGP at the recipient will not process the file and produce an output file. Instead, the recipient is told that the message is for display only and asked whether or not to display it now. PGP displays the message one screen at a time, in a manner similar to the DOS command:

MORE <*filename*

Even if the sender hasn't used the -m option, the recipient can force a similar behavior by using that option. In this case, PGP automatically displays its output one screen at a time. At the end, the user is asked whether or not to save the output permanently.

Typically, when pgp is presented with a file to decrypt or verify a signature, the file ends in .pgp or .asc depending on whether or not the file is in ASCII armor format. The decrypted file is given the same name without the .pgp or .asc. The -p option allows the user to recover the exact file name provided by the sender of this file.

The -f option enables you to specify the input and output files for a PGP operation in the style of a UNIX filter. Here's an example of how you could use this feature. When PGP validates a cleartext signature, it generates a new file, without the signature. If you don't need an unsigned copy of the file, or if you are writing a "Verify Clear Signature" feature into a mail or news reader, this gives you a file to delete, or a bunch of text on the screen to ignore.

To validate the file name.asc without generating new output, use

```
pgp -f <name.asc >nul
```

PGP displays the validity of the signature without generating a new file.

The -l option added to a pgp command forces a kind of debug mode, with more information displayed on the screen. Unless you have a copy of the source listing, you are likely to find this extra information meaningless.

Command-Line Flags and Parameters

The command-line flag is a PGP feature that enables a user to specify the value of a particular flag as part of a command line. A command line flag consists of a plus sign (+) followed by the flag name. Command-line flags include:

- Batch: When this flag is set PGP does not ask unnecessary questions or prompt for alternate file names. This is useful for batch mode operation of PGP. Example:

```
pgp +batchmode cipherfile
```

- Force: When this flag is set, PGP assumes the answer yes in response to the confirmation request to overwrite an existing file or when removing a key from the keyring via the -kr command. Again, this is useful for batch operation. Example:

```
pgp -kr +force Smith
```

- Nomanual: The freeware versions of PGP are supposed to be, and almost always are, distributed with the two-volume set of documentation prepared by Phil Zimmermann. To discourage distribution of PGP without the documentation, some implementations of PGP will not generate key pairs unless the documentation is somewhere on the same disk as PGP. For users with very limited memory, the nomanual flag is provided. It is used in the following command:

```
pgp -kg +nomanual
```

A command line parameter has the form

```
+parameter=value
```

The most common use of this form is to change the value of a parameter in the config.txt file, as explained in Section 8.4. One other parameter is the encrypttoself option. When this option is selected in conjunction with the -e command option, PGP includes you as one of the recipients. The convenience of this option is that you don't need to keep a plaintext copy of a message that you sent. You can keep the ciphertext copy and decrypt it whenever you need access to the plaintext. Example:

```
pgp -eta +encrypttoself=on filename userid
```

In some implementations of PGP, this parameter will not work unless you have set correctly the variable MyName in your config.txt file (see Section 8.4).

8.4   THE CONFIG.TXT FILE

The config.txt file comes as part of your DOS or UNIX PGP installation. It contains parameters that control the operation of PGP. Table 8.5 lists the parameters in the config.txt file and their default values. You can change any of these values by editing the config.txt file.

Another way to change a configuration parameter is with the use of a command-line parameter. For example, the following two commands produce the same operation:

```
pgp -e +armor=on message.txt smith
pgp -ea message.txt smith
```

The first of these commands also has the effect of changing the Armor parameter in the config.txt file to "on". Note that the config.txt keywords are case-insensitive (e.g., +armor=on is the same as +ARMOR=on) and can be abbreviated to unique prefixes (e.g., +v=2 is the same as +verbose=2).

Armor

When this parameter is on, PGP produces ciphertext and keys in ASCII armor format, suitable for handling by e-mail

Table **8.5**

config.txt Parameters

Parameter	Default Value	Description
Armor	off	When on, always produces ASCII armor output
ArmorLines	720	Maximum number of lines per transport armor file
BakRing	""	Pathname for backup secret key ring
Cert_Depth	4	How many levels of introducers allowed
CharSet	nonconv (no character conversion)	Character set for displaying messages and converting text files
ClearSig	on	Enable signed messages to be encapsulated as clear text
Comment	null	When defined, produces a comment line in all ASCII armor output
Completes_Needed	1	Number of completely trusted signatures required
Compress	on	Indicates whether to suppress compression
Interactive	off	Ask for confirmation for key adds
KeepBinary	off	Decrypt will not delete intermediate .pgp file
Language	en	Language for displaying prompts, warnings, and advisories
Marginals_Needed	2	Number of marginally trusted signatures required

Table **8.5** *(continued)*

config.txt Parameters

Parameter	Default Value	Description
MyName	—	User ID for secret key for signing
Pager	""	File viewing program for viewing messages with -m option
pkcs_compat	1	Level of compatibility with other versions of PGP
PubRing	c:\pgp\pubring.pgp	Pathname for default public key ring
Randseed	c:\pgp\randseed.bin	Pathname for random number seed file
SecRing	c:\pgp\secring.pgp	Pathname for default secret key ring
Showpass	off	Indicates whether to display password when user types it
TextMode	off	When on, uses the -t option whenever possible
TMP	""	Directory name for PGP scratch files
TZFix	0	Number of hours to add to system time to get GMT
Verbose	1	Amount of information supplied with diagnostic messages

facilities. This is equivalent to using the -a option all the time. If most of your use of PGP is for e-mail, you should enable this parameter.

ArmorLines

Some e-mail systems impose an upper limit on the size of messages that can be transported. By default, PGP produces output that is limited to 720 lines of ASCII text. If a larger file is produced, then PGP breaks it up into pieces labeled .as1, .as2, and so on. If you set this parameter to 0, PGP will not break up the file, no matter how big it is.

BakRing

This parameter contains the path name for the backup secret key ring if one is maintained by the user. PGP uses the backup ring during the -kc command to verify the user's public key. The backup should be kept on a write-protected medium. The most convenient location is a write-protected floppy disk. In that case, the user can set the BakRing parameter to a:\secring.pgp

Cert_Depth

This parameter gets into a subtle area of key management. Recall that there are two trust-related parameters associated with a key. One is the OwnerTrust value, which reflects the trust that you have in the owner of this key to sign other keys. The other is KeyLegitimacy, which determines whether you believe that this key in fact belongs to the user indicated by this User ID. In order to be able to use someone else as an introducer, you must have two things: (1) you must be convinced that you have the introducer's valid key (key legitimacy), and (2) you must trust the person to act as an introducer (owner trust).

The OwnerTrust assigned to a key must be decided by you specifically for each key on your public key ring. It makes no sense to assign owner trust unless you know the key is a valid key for that person. Key validity, or legitimacy, is decided on the basis of the signatures attached to the key. For example, suppose that Bob's key is on your key ring. If you personally know that this key is valid for Bob (you did the exchange with the other person), then you can sign it; this is referred to as depth 1. Say that you have declared Bob completely trusted and Bob has signed Alice's key. Then the legitimacy of Alice's key is established at depth 2. Further suppose that you have designated Alice as a trusted introducer and she has signed Ted's key. Now we are at depth 3. Here is how it works. You believe Ted's key is valid (i.e., it belongs to the User ID we associated with Ted) because Alice signed it and you trust Alice. You know that the signature is really Alice's

because you believe Alice's key is valid and you trust Alice. You
believe Alice's key is valid because Bob signed it and you trust
Bob. You believe that the signature is really Bob's because you
believe Bob's key is valid. Finally, you believe Bob's key is valid
because you signed it.[3]

If you know all of your trusted introducers personally, and
have signed their keys, then you will never have a key at a depth
of greater than 2. For most users, it is a good practice to sign
the keys of all your trusted introducers. These considerations of
depth should only come into play for someone managing a very
large key ring.

CharSet

This parameter indicates the character set normally used on
your machine. This determines what character conversions are
performed by PGP when the -t option is used. PGP uses the
LATIN1 alphabet internally, which is the most common. Other
possibilities are ALT-CODES (used by Russian MS-DOS systems),
ASCII, and CP850 (used by most Western European languages on
standard MS-DOS systems).

ClearSig

When this parameter is on, clear signing is used for the -sta
command option. The default for this value depends on the implementation; you should check your implementation. For example,
the default value of clearsig is off for PGP 2.3a and is on for PGP
2.6 and 2.7.

Comment

If the line

```
comment = <string>
```

appears in the `config.txt` file, then the line

```
Comment: <string>
```

---

[3] Actually, you the reader signed Bob's key because you believe it to be valid, but
your PGP believes the key is valid because you signed it!

will appear in any ASCII armor output, including encrypted files
and signed files. The comment line appears just after the Version:
line. This feature enables you to put a fixed comment in all ASCII
armor files. To place a comment that is specific to a particular file,
you need to use the +comment= command line parameter.

Completes_Needed

This parameter specifies how many completely trusted signatures are needed on a Key-ID/User-ID combination before PGP
will declare that the combination is valid. The default is 1 signature, but you may set this at any number you wish.

Compress

Normally, PGP compresses a file when it is processed for
sending. PGP compresses after signing (if a signature is present)
and before encrypting (if encryption is used). For the typical user,
there is no reason not to use compression. A software developer
may find it useful to disable this feature for debugging purposes.

Interactive

By default, when you add a keyfile to your public key ring,
PGP adds all keys from that file to your ring. If you first set
Interactive = on, then PGP will ask you, for each key in the file,
whether you want to add that key to your ring.

This feature is useful when you obtain a key file with a number of keys in it. For example, every implementation of PGP comes
with a keys.asc file with keys for the various developers. You
may want to add one or two of these, such as Phil Zimmermann's
key, but, for example, have no need for the key of Branko Lankester. If the key file is large, it is easier to reject keys one at a time
via PGP prompt than to add all the keys and then remove the unwanted ones.

KeepBinary

If you have received an encrypted file in ASCII armor format
and ask PGP to decrypt it, PGP first removes the ASCII armor to

recover the binary encrypted file. This binary file is temporarily stored in a .pgp file. After decryption, the .pgp file is deleted. If you wish to retain this binary file, the KeepBinary parameter must be set to on.

Language

Many of the prompts, warnings, and advisories issued by PGP to the user have been translated into a number of foreign languages, including Spanish, Dutch, German, French, Italian, Russian, Latvian, Lithuanian, and Esperanto. These translations are stored in a separate file, language.txt, which comes with many implementations of PGP and is available separately for use with other implementations. If the user sets the Language parameter to refer to one of these languages, then PGP displays information as much as possible in the selected language. Information for which no translation is available is presented in English.

Marginals_Needed

This parameter specifies how many marginally trusted signatures are needed on a Key-ID/User-ID combination before PGP declares that the combination is valid. The default is 2 signatures, but you may set this at any number you wish.

MyName

If you have more than one secret key, then you may specify which key to use for any command that requires the use of a secret key. If you don't specify a key, then a default secret key is used. Unless otherwise specified, the default secret key is the one most recently added to your secret key ring (the first key listed when all of your secret keys are displayed). You can specify a different default secret key with the MyName parameter. This parameter specifies the User ID associated with the desired key.

Pager

If the recipient specifies the -m option when decrypting an incoming file, the plaintext is displayed on the screen rather than

being sent to a file. PGP displays the message one screen at a
time, in a manner similar to the DOS command:

MORE <*filename*

The user hits the space key to see each succeeding page. The Pager
parameter allows the user to specify a more powerful display utility than the primitive MORE capability. One example is the popular
shareware utility list.com.

This option applies only to the use of the -m option by the
recipient. If the sender used the -m option, which forces the recipient to receive the output via display rather than to disk, then PGP
always uses the MORE capability. The recipient has the option of
saving the plaintext to a file after viewing.

pkcs-compat

This option specifies that the formats to be used for signatures, public keys, and other PGP data structures. The options are:

- pkcs_compat = 1:   Generates output that is understand-
                     able by PGP Versions 2.6 and 2.7 and
                     later versions, but is not understand-
                     able by PGP Versions 2.3 and earlier.

- pkcs_compat = 2:   Generates output that is understand-
                     able by all versions of PGP.

This option is only found in some implementations, such as
ViaCrypt 2.7. Its purpose is to deal with the compatibility issues
raised by the introduction of PGP 2.6 from MIT (see Chapter 1 for
a discussion).

PubRing

This parameter enables the user to specify a different path
name for the default public key ring. You can even specify that
your public key ring is on a diskette drive rather than the system's
hard disk. The advantage of this is that essential information
about your encrypted correspondence isn't left on your system
where it might be accessible to others.

Randseed

The random number seed file, `randseed.bin`, is by default in the same directory as your `config.txt` file. PGP uses the `randseed.bin` file when generating public/secret key pairs and session keys. Knowledge of the contents of this file could theoretically make it easier for an opponent to defeat PGP. If you fear that someone may gain access to your system, the Randseed parameter enables you to specify a different pathname. If you wish to keep this file on a floppy disk, then use the following definition:

```
RANDSEED = "a:randseed.bin"
```

SecRing

This parameter enables the user to specify a different path name for the default secret key ring. You can specify that your secret key ring is on a diskette drive rather than the system's hard disk. Even though your secret key is safe so long as you use an effective passphrase, you may prefer the extra security of keeping your secret key ring on a removable floppy disk.

ShowPass

As with virtually all programs and systems that require a password, PGP disables the character echo function when you enter your passphrase, so that it doesn't show up on your screen. This prevents the obvious security risk of over-the-shoulder eavesdropping. Of course, in the privacy of your own home that may not be much of a risk (you don't have your back to a window do you?). Some people may find it convenient to see their passphrase as they type it, especially if they have a long passphrase. Furthermore, there are typing-impaired individuals who have difficulty typing without seeing what they are typing. The ShowPass parameter meets this need.

TextMode

This parameter is equivalent to the -t command option. Recall that the -t option tells PGP to treat the input as an ASCII text file. When this option is present, PGP first converts the input to *canonical form*. Later, when the message is received on another system and the original file is recovered, PGP converts from canonical form to the local text format. Primarily, these conversions have to do with the proper handling of carriage returns and line feeds, as explained in Chapter 4. When the TextMode parameter is on, PGP always assumes the -t option. If PGP detects that the file isn't text, then it doesn't attempt the conversion.

This parameter is useful if most of your messages are text files.

TMP

Normally, PGP places files that it uses temporarily in the same directory as the `config.txt` file. If you have a RAM disk, the files can be placed there instead. This speeds up the operation a bit and is somewhat more secure.

TZFix

This parameter is used to correct the time provided by the operating system to PGP for use in time stamping keys and signature certificates. Whether or not this parameter is needed depends on how your system is configured. See the documentation that comes with your implementation of PGP for details.

Verbose

There are three options for the amount of information PGP provides during the execution of a command:

0 Display messages only if there is a problem
1 Normal default setting. Displays a reasonable amount of detail in diagnostic or advisory messages
2 Displays a maximum amount of information, usually to help diagnose problems in PGP.

It is probably best to stick with the default value of 1. At the beginning, you might want to set this parameter to 2 until you are comfortable using PGP.

8.5 USING A DOS SHELL

The command-line interface for DOS PGP enables the user to exploit the full power of PGP; all commands and command options are available. However, many people find this primitive interface awkward and user-unfriendly. One alternative is to use a Windows front-end interface; this approach is described in Chapter 11.

Another approach is to use a PGP DOS shell. In essence, a shell program provides a friendlier interface to some underlying command-line program. The advantage of a DOS shell program is that it can run directly under DOS; Windows isn't required. Thus, virtually all machines that can run DOS PGP can also run a DOS shell, including older 640K RAM XTs and other pre-386 machines. There are still many millions of these machines out there worldwide.

One excellent example of a DOS shell for PGP, and perhaps the most popular one, is PGPShell, developed by James Still. This section summarizes PGPShell.

Main Menu

When you invoke PGPShell, following a banner page, you are presented with the main menu (Figure 8.1). PGPShell organizes all of the PGP functions into four main categories. PGPShell always assumes the use of the -t and -a options.

In the main menu, and in all the other windows, the user can navigate with tab keys or arrow keys, and can select items using the mouse.

Encrypt a Message

When you choose the first option (Encrypt a Message), PGPShell replaces the main menu with a list of User IDs found on your public key ring (Figure 8.2). You can select one or more recipients by hitting the space bar while the pointer is at a particular User ID. After finishing selection, PGPShell displays, on the same screen that shows your User ID selection, the message:

```
Create a New Message?
```

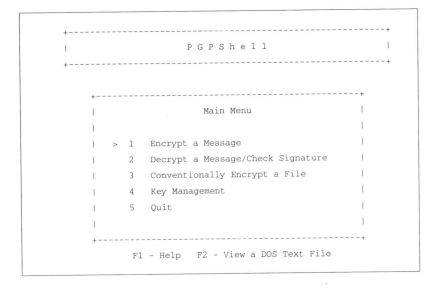

Fig **8.1**   PGPShell Main Menu

If you answer yes, you are moved into a simple text editor embedded in PGPShell. This is very convenient for correspondence and short notes. You don't have to prepare messages ahead of time outside of PGP, store them in text files, and then invoke PGP. Instead, with PGPShell, you can create messages on the fly.

If you answer no, PGPShell provides a convenient interface for selecting a text file in any directory on your system.

Once you have either prepared a new text file or selected an existing text file, PGPShell presents a menu of the following options:

- Sign the message with your secret key: This is equivalent to the PGP -s command option. If you select this option, you are prompted for your secret key.
- Shred the original after encryption: This option uses the -w command option to wipe out the original file so that only the ciphertext is retained.
- Recipient should view on-screen only: This is equivalent to the sender's use of the -m command option.

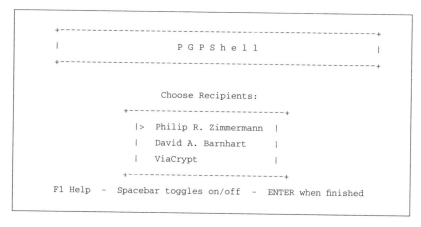

```
    +----------------------------------------------------------+
    |                    P G P S h e l l                       |
    +----------------------------------------------------------+

                     Choose Recipients:
            +----------------------------+
            |>  Philip R. Zimmermann   |
            |   David A. Barnhart      |
            |   ViaCrypt               |
            +----------------------------+
  F1 Help  -  Spacebar toggles on/off  -  ENTER when finished
```

Fig **8.2**   PGPShell: Encrypt a Message

- Clear sign the message: This option uses the clearsig=on feature of PGP. Unlike using this option directly in PGP, PGPShell doesn't permanently toggle you to the clear sig=on state.

The user can choose one or more of the above options, or none of them. By default, the message is also encrypted unless the clearsig option is selected.

Thus, PGPShell provides a convenient way to choose the most common command option combinations for message encryption.

Decrypt a Message/Check Signature

When you choose the second option from the main menu, PGPShell replaces the main menu with a layout that allows you to select a file in any directory for decryption (Figure 8.3). Once you have selected a file, PGPShell presents a menu of the following options:

- Leave the signature on the message intact: This is equivalent to the PGP -d command.
- Recover the original plaintext while decrypting: This is equivalent to the PGP -p command and causes PGP to save the decrypted plaintext with the original filename.

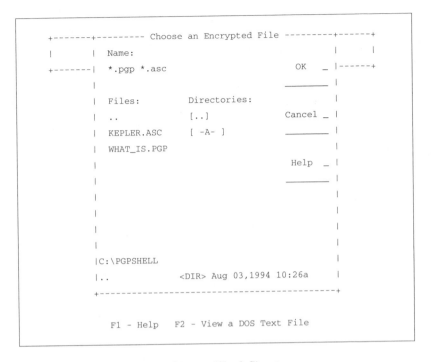

Fig **8.3**   PGPShell: Decrypt a Message/Check Signature

- Detach signature certification from message: This option
  uses the PGP -b command and creates a separate .sig file
  that contains the signature attached to the ciphertext file.
- Don't write to a file; view on-screen only: This is equivalent
  to the recipient's use of the -m option.

Once again, PGPShell provides the common options in a convenient form.

Conventionally Encrypt a File

This function is similar to the message encryption option, but
without allowing the range of options. When the user selects this
option, PGPShell presents a window that allows the user to select
a file (Figure 8.4). The user is then prompted for a passphrase and
the file is encrypted. The convenience of this command, compared

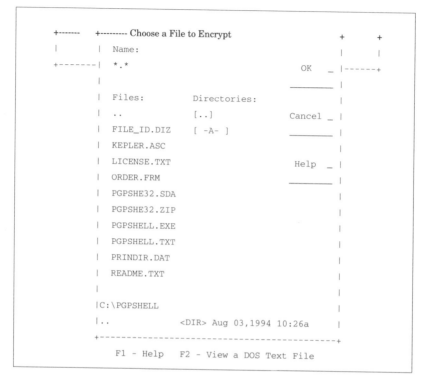

```
+-------    +--------- Choose a File to Encrypt              +       +
|          |  Name:                                          |       |
+-------|  *.*                                   OK    _  |------+
          |                                            _____  |
          |  Files:          Directories:                       |
          |  ..               [..]             Cancel _  |
          |  FILE_ID.DIZ      [ -A- ]           _____  |
          |  KEPLER.ASC                                        |
          |  LICENSE.TXT                         Help   _  |
          |  ORDER.FRM                          _____  |
          |  PGPSHE32.SDA                                      |
          |  PGPSHE32.ZIP                                      |
          |  PGPSHELL.EXE                                      |
          |  PGPSHELL.TXT                                      |
          |  PRINDIR.DAT                                       |
          |  README.TXT                                        |
          |                                                    |
          |C:\PGPSHELL                                         |
          |..                 <DIR> Aug 03,1994 10:26a        |
          +----------------------------------------------+
               F1 - Help   F2 - View a DOS Text File
```

Fig **8.4**   PGPShell: Conventionally Encrypt a File

to using PGP directly, is the ability to navigate quickly through
your directories to select a file.

Key Management

It is in the key management portion of PGPShell that we
see the greatest improvement over the use of the command-line
interface.

Figure 8.5 shows the top-level PGPShell display for key management. The upper left-hand corner displays a list of User IDs for
the keys on your public key ring. You can select one or more keys
from your ring for any operation.

The lower portion of the display provides information on the

```
z-----------------------++-----------------------------------------------+
|>  Philip R. Zimmermann ||    F1 - Help                                  |
|                        ||                                               |
|   David A. Barnhart    ||    F2 - Edit/Copy key currently selected      |
|                        ||                                               |
|   ViaCrypt             ||    F3 - Compose message to checkmarked recipients |
|                        ||                                               |
|   Dudley Dos           ||    F4 - Add a new key to current key ring     |
+------------------------+|    F5 - Choose a different PGP key ring       |
                         +-----------------------------------------------+

+------------------------------------------------------------------------+
|      UserID: Philip R. Zimmermann                                       |
|      E-mail: prz@acm.org                    KeyID: C7A966DD             |
|      Fingerprint: 9E 94 45 13 39 83 5F 70   7B E7 D8 ED C4 BE 5A A6     |
|                                                                         |
|      Signatures Attached:             Your Trust of This Person:        |
|                                                                         |
|      Dudley Dos                              ultimate                   |
|      David A. Barnhart                       unknown                    |
|      (KeyID: 8DE722D9)                       undefined                  |
|      (KeyID: 865AA7F3)                       undefined                  |
|      (KeyID: FF67F70B)                       undefined                  |
|                                                                         |
| Other signatures exist but not displayed...                            |
| Your personal trust of Philip R. Zimmermann is: complete               |
| PGP has determined the validity (trustworthiness) to be: complete      |
+------------------------------------------------------------------------+
      Spacebar to checkmark UserID - Arrow or mouse to view keys - ESC to quit
```

Fig **8.5**   PGPShell: Key Management

current key (the one pointed to in the User ID list). This display is certainly more convenient for viewing than the ordinary DOS PGP display. The display shows:

- Name portion of User ID
- Key ID
- E-mail address portion of User ID
- Fingerprint
- A list of all signatures and the level of trust for signing that you have assigned to each key owner

- The level of trust you have assigned to the owner of this key
- The validity of this key as computed by PGP on the basis of the attached signatures

The upper right-hand portion of the display lists the operations that can be invoked by function key. Each operation is invoked for the key or keys selected form the User ID list. Let us examine each of these operations in turn

Edit/Copy Key Currently Selected   When you press the F2 key, PGPShell overlays the key management display with a menu listing the following options:

1. Delete this key from your key ring.
2. Copy this key to an external file.
3. Indicate your trust in this person.
4. Certify this key as valid.
5. Remove signature(s) from this key
6. Disable or reenable this key

In each case, PGPShell drops back down to the PGP dialogue to complete the operation and then goes back to the PGPShell key management display.

Compose Message to Checkmarked Recipients   This convenient option accomplishes the same function as the Encrypt a Message option from the main menu. After you select one or more User IDs, you can either compose a new message with the built-in editor or choose a file.

Add a New Key to Current Key Ring   When this function is selected, PGPShell enables you to select a file containing one or more keys, which are then added to the current key ring.

Choose a Different PGP Key Ring   When this function is selected, PGPShell enables you to select any public or secret key ring in any directory.

Macintosh PGP: Getting Started

T his chapter and the next examine the Macintosh implementation of PGP. This chapter provides a step-by-step look at the basics. Follow the sequence of operations in this chapter and you will be ready to use MacPGP.[1]

PGP IN A NUTSHELL

If you are reading this section first, before reading Part I, and you have no familiarity with PGP, please read this box. PGP (Pretty Good Privacy) is a software package that does two major things:

1. Provides confidentiality for messages sent by electronic mail: Only the sender and receiver can read the message.
2. Enables the sender to digitally sign a message so that the receiver knows that the message hasn't come from an impostor and hasn't been altered.

Both services rely on a scheme known as public-key encryption. The essence of this scheme is as follows: Everyone using PGP has two keys: one public key, which anyone is allowed to know, and one secret key, which is kept secret by the user.

Any message can be scrambled, or encrypted, in such a way that only the recipient can unscramble it. The sender performs a set of operations to encrypt the message that involves the use of the intended

---

[1] The examples in this chapter were generated using MacPGP 2.6, developed at MIT. Other MacPGP versions have virtually identical user interfaces.

recipient's public key. The recipient is then able to decrypt the message using his or her secret key.

Any message can be signed by performing an operation involving the signer's secret key. The signature can subsequently be checked by performing an operation involving the signer's public key. Therefore, when you send a message, you can sign it with your secret key, and any recipient can verify your signature using your public key.

To use PGP successfully, you must do three things:

1. Keep your secret key secret: Don't let anyone else learn it.
2. Make sure that all potential correspondents have your public key.
3. Get the public key of each potential correspondent.

9.1 GETTING STARTED

This chapter takes you through a series of steps following installation of MacPGP on your system. The installation itself depends somewhat on which version of MacPGP you have. Once you are done with the installation, you should have at least the following files in the folder that you use, which should be called "MacPGP2.6 Folder."

- config.txt: Contains some configuration parameters that can be used to tailor PGP's operation. For now, leave the default settings as they are.
- randseed.bin: Used by MacPGP in the random-number generation process; you don't need to be concerned with it.
- keys.asc: Contains the public keys of some of MacPGP's developers.

Once you have started to use MacPGP, it generates four more files in the same folder:

- pubring.pgp: Your default public key ring.
- pubring.bak: Your default backup public key ring; MacPGP automatically updates this ring so that it is one change behind pubring.pgp.
- secring.pgp: Your default secret key ring.
- secring.bak: Your default backup secret key ring; MacPGP automatically updates this ring so that it is one change behind secring.pgp.

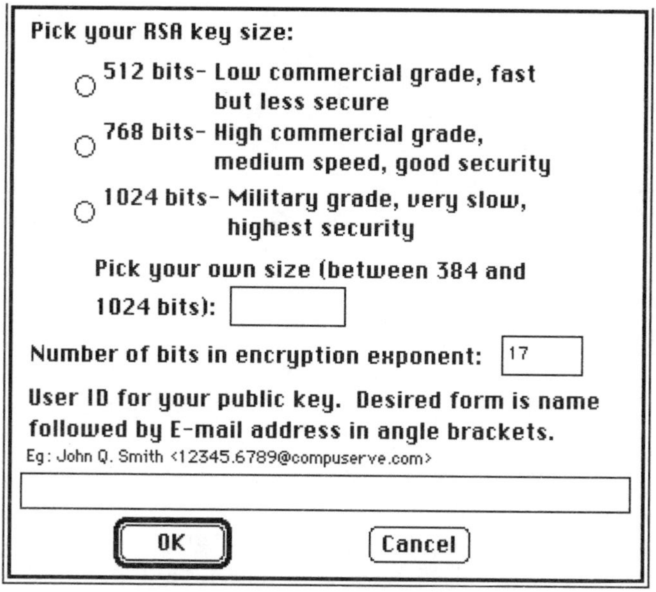

Pick your RSA key size:

○ 512 bits– Low commercial grade, fast
    but less secure

○ 768 bits– High commercial grade,
    medium speed, good security

○ 1024 bits– Military grade, very slow,
    highest security

Pick your own size (between 384 and
1024 bits): [   ]

Number of bits in encryption exponent: [17   ]

User ID for your public key. Desired form is name
followed by E-mail address in angle brackets.
Eg: John Q. Smith <12345.6789@compuserve.com>

[   ]

(**OK**)   (Cancel)

Fig **9.1**   Key Generation Window

You invoke MacPGP by double-clicking on the MacPGP26 application. When the application is loaded, it displays a window labeled "PGP Messages" and a menu bar with four options:

- File: Functions for encrypting and decrypting files and other file-related operations.
- Edit: Cut, copy, paste, and clear operations.
- Key: Key management operations.
- Options: Configuration options.

9.2 KEY GENERATION

The first step is to generate a secret/public key pair. Choose the "Generate Key" option under the "Key" pull down menu. MacPGP responds with the display of Figure 9.1.

Use the upper part of the window to pick a key size. As you can see, the larger the key size, the more secure will be your communication. It takes noticeably longer to generate larger keys,

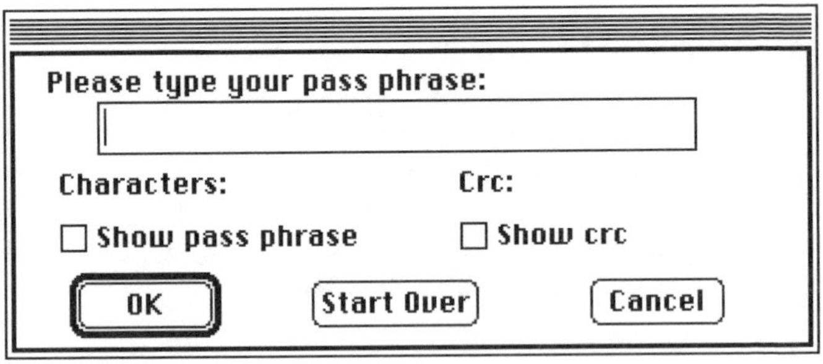

Please type your pass phrase:

```
|
```

Characters: Crc:

☐ Show pass phrase   ☐ Show crc

[OK]   [Start Over]   [Cancel]

Fig **9.2**   Passphrase Window

but key generation is a one-time procedure. The time to prepare messages for sending or to process received messages doesn't change much with the different key sizes. Therefore, always select 1024 bits.

You can also pick the number of bits in the encryption exponent, a matter that is discussed in Chapter 5. Most people are happy to leave this at the default of 17 bits.

You are also asked for a User ID. For our example we use:

```
Moira McIntosh <mm@apple.net>
```

After you click OK, MacPGP prompts you for a passphrase (Figure 9.2). This is an important step. Any time you use your secret key, MacPGP needs your passphrase to retrieve it. The passphrase should be something that is (1) easy to remember so that you don't have to write it down but (2) difficult to guess. Finding a passphrase that meets both criteria isn't as easy as it might sound. I highly recommend you read through Chapter 13 at some point. For now, take your best shot; you can always change your passphrase later without changing your key.

Once you have entered a passphrase, MacPGP displays the following message in the PGP Message Window:

```
We need to generate 560 random bits. This is done
by measuring the time intervals between your key-
strokes. Please  enter some random text on your
keyboard until you hear the beep:
```

Type anything you like at a normal pace. MacPGP uses the timing and the actual characters you enter to generate random numbers needed in the key generation process. While you are typing, you see a number on the screen that counts down to 0. MacPGP then beeps you and issues the following in the message window:

```
    0 * -Enough, thank you.
. . . . . . . . .++++  . . . . . . . .++++
Key generation completed.
```

The series of pluses and dots are just an indication that MacPGP is working on the key generation.

9.3 SIGNING YOUR KEY

Before doing anything else with MacPGP, you should sign your public key. Your signature on your key guarantees that no one can tamper with your key or User ID without detection. MacPGP uses your secret key to sign your public key. Select "Certify Key" from the Key menu. MacPGP then asks you to select a particular public key ring where it looks for the key to be certified. Select pubring.pgp.

MacPGP then displays the contents of your public key ring (Figure 9.3) and asks you to select a key for certification. At this point, the only key on this ring is your own public key, and that is the one you wish to sign, so click on that key.

If you have more than one secret key, MacPGP at this point asks you to pick one. In this case, you only have one secret key. MacPGP retrieves that key and then displays the warning message of Figure 9.4.

When you sign a key, yours or someone else's, you are certifying that this key belongs to the person identified by the User ID in question. So, to make sure, MacPGP asks if you are absolutely certain. If you are certain, you answer MacPGP's question with a "yes" and MacPGP responds by prompting you for your passphrase. Whenever you sign a message or a public key, MacPGP must use

```
          Macintosh HD:MacPGP Folder:pubring.pgp
Certify which key?
pub 1024/694C1FFD 1994/08/09 Moira McIntosh <mm@apple.net>   ⬆
                                                             
                                                             
                                                             
                                                             ⬇
Display only uids    [|                        ]  [Redisplay]
containing:
           [   OK   ]          [Cancel]
```

Fig **9.3**   Key Signing Window

your secret key, and to get your secret key it needs your passphrase. Enter your passphrase and MacPGP completes the signing operation and displays the following in the message window:

```
Pass phrase is good.   Just a moment....
Key signature certificate added.
```

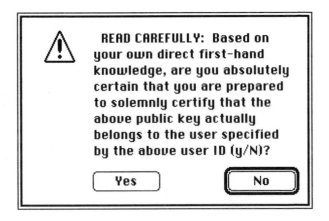

Fig **9.4**   Key-Signing Prompt

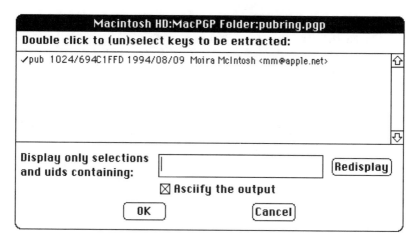

Fig **9.5**   Key Extraction Window

9.4 EXTRACTING YOUR KEY

Your correspondents need your public key in order to send you encrypted messages and to verify your signature on your messages to them. Now that you have signed your key, extract it into a text file, which can then be sent to potential correspondents or posted on a public key server.

Select "Extract Key" from the Key menu. MacPGP then asks you to select a particular public key ring where it will look for the key to be certified. Select pubring.pgp, and MacPGP then asks you to select one or more keys, as shown in Figure 9.5. Double click to select your public key; whenever you select a key from a window such as Figure 9.5, a check mark appears to the left of each selected key. Also check the box, "Asciify the output;" this will produce a text file that is suitable for e-mailing. MacPGP then asks you to indicate a file name and folder for the extracted key. Enter mykey, and MacPGP responds in the message window:

```
Extracting from key ring: 'Macintosh HD:MacPGP
Folder:pubring.pgp', userid "0x69
4C1FFD".
```

(continued)

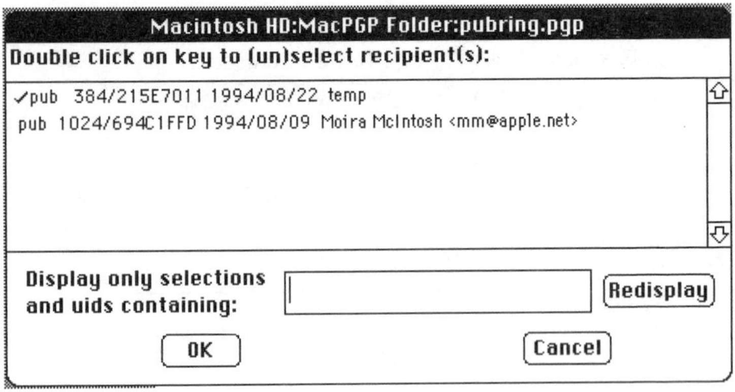

```
▓▓▓▓▓▓▓▓ Macintosh HD:MacPGP Folder:pubring.pgp ▓▓▓▓▓▓▓▓
Double click on key to (un)select recipient(s):
┌──────────────────────────────────────────────────────┬─┐
│✓pub  384/215E7011 1994/08/22 temp                      │⇧│
│ pub 1024/694C1FFD 1994/08/09 Moira McIntosh <mm@apple.net>│ │
│                                                        │ │
│                                                        │ │
│                                                        │⇩│
└──────────────────────────────────────────────────────┴─┘
 Display only selections  ┌──────────────────────┐ ⎡Redisplay⎤
 and uids containing:      │                      │ ⎣         ⎦
          ⎡   OK   ⎤                       ⎡ Cancel ⎤
```

Fig **9.6**   Select Recipients Window

```
Key for user ID: Moira McIntosh <mm@apple.net>
1024-bit key, Key ID 694C1FFD, created 1994/08/09
Key extracted to file 'Macintosh HD:MacPGPFolder:mykey.pgp'.
pgp -a"Macintosh HD:MacPGP Folder:mykey.pgp" +force=ON
+batchmode=ON
Transport armor file: Macintosh HD:MacPGP Folder:mykey.asc
```

Here is a print-out of the file `mykey.asc`:

```
-----BEGIN PGP PUBLIC KEY BLOCK-----
Version: 2.6

mQCPAi5H578AAAEEANVnSCWuVWS8XGq2PPrvZQurXxhAbxDAl9tLYkus1zykutNf
St2WTw36uuJfHF6muE4IFHL8178YBBrVqgBIn3/fvqWRV0TVE3WKdp56QTRG+m8t
V16ZlXMiY7L76BuvNEK2zVzCVBxtSRCLZ8zQSqg5Am4zetPdJ3hg8FFpTB/9ABEB
AAG0HU1vaXJhIE1jSW50b3NoIDxtbUBhcHBsZS5uZXQ+iQCVAgUQLkiFenhg8FFp
TB/9AQF0sgP8CGkNBk48i0cLyKCbazQD/8QzpLt0OxDllGjKTj3m2cXhMbTZzH1G
LHiewGy31TEnVc7bnwai+HHJ3mkXz9YqzHPAFOog+pyKDL2kNPPC2GjESxkM7Q1A
NDRtdWjtqiIdzVlcrKj6Q8uh6jSmVeODMSYOnnzX3/dpvexC0ElTaR4=
=q56i
-----END PGP PUBLIC KEY BLOCK-----
```

When this file is read by another user's PGP, it can be converted into the proper format and stored on a public key ring.

9.5 PREPARING A MESSAGE FOR TRANSMISSION

You now have your public and secret keys organized and ready for use. Before actually exchanging messages with others, let us go through a little practice session. Fortunately, MacPGP makes this very easy to do by allowing multiple keys on your secret key ring. You can create a second public/secret key pair with a different User ID. Now you have two "personalities" and the two can exchange messages.

First, perform the key generation process again. Following the steps outlined previously, MacPGP creates a new pair of keys and stores them on your two key rings. To keep things simple, choose a 512-bit key with a User ID of temp and a passphrase of temp. Now, let us prepare a message from you to temp.

As input for this exercise, you can use any file on your system. For example, let us use the file config.txt. It's handy because it is in the same folder as MacPGP and it is a text file, so you will be able to compare the input and the output.

Select the Encrypt/Sign option from the File menu. MacPGP first asks you to select a file, and then displays your public key ring and asks you to double-click on one more recipients. As Figure 9.6 shows, your public key ring now contains two keys. Choose the key for User Id "temp" and a check mark appears next to the key.

MacPGP next displays the window of Figure 9.7. The display reflects the choices that have been made: the input file is config.txt, the sender is Moira McIntosh, and the recipient is user "temp." In the upper left-hand of the window, select the Encrypt and sign entry to cause MacPGP to encrypt the file for the recipient and to sign it on behalf of the sender. On the right-hand side, check the following boxes:

- Treat source file as text: Always do this if in fact the source file is a text file, to ensure compatibility between user systems.
- Produce output in ASCII radix-64 format: This ensures that the message is protected from damage during e-mail handling.

After you select the Do It button, MacPGP prompts you for

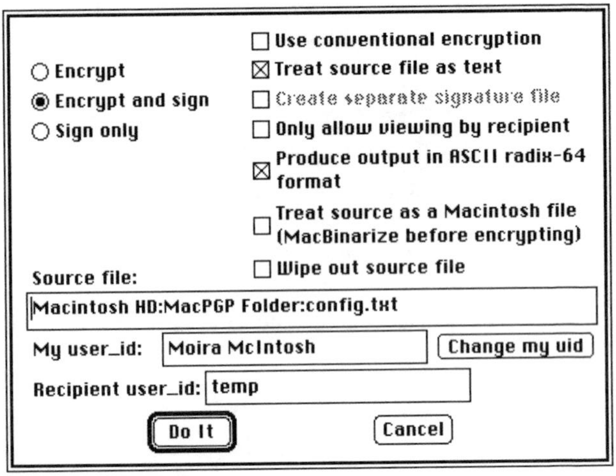

Fig **9.7**   Encrypt and Sign Window

your passphrase, in order to make the signature; this is the same
prompt we saw before for signing a key (Figure 9.2). MacPGP
responds in the message window:

```
Pass phrase is good.
Key for user ID: Moira McIntosh <mm@apple.net>
1024-bit key, Key ID 88E7A835, created 1994/08/09
Just a moment....

Recipients' public key(s) will be used to encrypt.
Key for user ID: temp
512-bit key, Key ID 694C1FFD, created 1994/08/10
.
Transport armor file: Macintosh HD:MacPGP
     Folder:config.txt.asc
```

This shows that the secret key for Moira McIntosh was used
to sign the message, and that the public key for user temp was
used for encrypting the message. The result is stored in the file
config.txt.asc. Unless told otherwise, MacPGP always creates a

file with the same name as the input file but ending in ".asc." The result is shown in Figure 9.8.

The result in Figure 9.8 appears to be gibberish and is indecipherable by anyone not in possession of temp's secret key. It has the additional feature that the file consists of nothing but printable characters. The file is formatted so that it can be transmitted through any e-mail system without risk of alteration. Thus, there is little danger of a change caused by the e-mail transfer process that would make it impossible to recover the original file. This is why it is referred to as a transport armor file: it is protected from damage during transport.

9.6 PROCESSING A RECEIVED MESSAGE

Once a transport armor file is prepared, it can be sent out as the body of an e-mail message. In fact, if you have a way of sending e-mail to yourself, you should do this. If not, let us just take the file config.asc and pretend that it arrived from an e-mail system. What we want to do now is the reverse of the sending operation, namely, decrypt the file using the receiver's (temp) secret key and then validate the signature using the sender's (Moira McIntosh) public key.

Incidentally, if you do send this file to yourself, you will be left with an incoming message that includes not only the contents of Figure 9.8 but also some header lines that indicate the sender, receiver, and subject of the message. No matter. PGP ignores anything that isn't enclosed between the lines:

```
-----BEGIN PGP MESSAGE-----
```

and

```
-----END PGP MESSAGE-----
```

So, we assume that temp has just received a message, which is now stored under the name config.asc, and wishes to recover a readable copy. Select the Open/Decrypt option from the File menu. MacPGP first asks you to select the file to be opened/decrypted and then displays the window of Figure 9.9. If it isn't already selected, select the first option. This tells MacPGP to take the file indicated

-----BEGIN PGP MESSAGE-----
Version: 2.6

hEwC4nC6HYjnqDUBAgCCl+gFAD2LQeGMkReu4ZNb8pGEIS8EpiEMym7xy7UKpYyX
aXgG3lvBS+R+HlWKPg9tn7nfQ/mItu3qxw41NsmIpgAACHscN9SS7yHc+P8kyv3a
/yEUl378uk6wjlSXYAhUTYTOlJn4MM+vw0lA9PSGYkYrVwth+nw9W8KYkpwCDGgK
TmZyRR8o8heC3pXz7CXriSYxteUo5d3+fbPFCs4bpJW8KpUurwM8lMG4DYAPehdz
VuOApODXQh9w7ebdP3CCxQ1jQRNNJzuGnaYEpJNT46tJ1VQgGXfH+hkYbEN30JCD
Z3y8XYtd1D8jR0PT8MbR7vVASIuVui9H9D2Au/cwoYx9apmnLtbzWMCafZsIdhPO
jRsNpYT3fIKBhQkHQrgiLVpQ+7KfxUqhFz0fHWZDMPWfNIlbLXuxVshhPCTdGe7J
0OFGANEe97r13mr8CV28CEl3dmfV7Gse4WsRs4zUQt35ENVS5UZy0zGUNFc3BOSz
MTAM2uXBT6MaXpWydYLGYGVh0k9fuTpA4lt+4GESPqCf7tBn2sHqRm+Qc3WDkbQf
XpcB0zVmlyEoSCvoKJrT6AzNP0hSNJxvqTcY+86HutRDECeDBU8M3TbALDVOMwDh
XpDUpbP7UxV7toCvaVgHY/XU/eVy5yuYxvkLoovSkImsmIXe1rJML/lS1pGyW2Ll
/xAxoaYwO/yGY9Hg8/wCOAZwOiz9lHKwliwudj0Hkapt7sq/lz8c8pGXkjhNd8EV
jcT+oItAPdyGZ0IcoWwPIYDLeLnmbxP7cq64UlPt8a2YvXqk/hOhvVhx5z6HeM+b
cVjN99sa+lVkZf2jTIwvQEQcMAg04I1LHZ6ZIfPAv9TbIa++j2oOoGxp7ck5+4Wp
6m0IB+RZy7JVg5XLgm6sYo7WYqXWSusqf8d4CpK+QOsvpQJqp/TZCA43+jex5T9p
bvrjDqg1GN9iqX6VU/E+FMDbTUj7POs+HdPeDW02SP7Xaq4YDW3lr55W45VJRC30
0r+J6B3Fr6TAFf/9vn/4+N1iNViOt861iTDcr4DWOhJB8wJhiS4aAi87OnWvknHJ
9+gvwV6LAKjJRfsqFDnEx2P0UjeoSeHsykfYfb2OsEFEtZGjpmx947zno6k36+N0
MnNmr9D8fh6di5mMUPBE0jHkuHmrvP+dt0oBnC+rKwZT1mEmDoxiCGKmDCK/gSk2
TnfR1CvSpUAbSooYo2QsKTmrje/5UfEe7/INTuCZs7MPEUMMCBC3wq1md4xFje1S
ytjBeTI/QU6ilgm7OLcDDA44D5o6g/DPJrEWmjhX5vvvL2K2X0afJuA2aU9GuxWV
ztjf5RbOQDO5icqzI6sWGTNMLDLthWvXS3jfNyodP86wgyWX7XElowIpJaUc3pcF
chpbDPhjgN2pm6mreqpY86uawlYm1d1jnIo+CIRvcyUyAUWAKMIE0pDdUfbJfnp2
yhU2YGQb8rhuD/wIQ+PSJN3M5755D/c1X9f3V31ROEWCzt1Jem15YXsdK9ju2U1V
A7AuJGpnhZUaC4BPPWaC12TfhgM0UTSCNhXTcpr/oGg63hDBqPq+cZycvEf2xA8g
IaASr881ZPBaoirP8SACmLpKRMfJ3n0TFqcaiaI11Z9uI5IssobTKUTwJxIItaKI
MLayigZ00RRvmrVi/XJafmc4YiyLk+53W2G9V8vDNkAyUYpwo8lG/dNSCJdrV8KW
AQDoFBSxEWx03y5HbD7Pxv5zN8eveveBgps0gVbmNZWDupJpcQG3FiAmgJN2EFTS
1NbJnbPVUcpKkckIl8mVfVu8TukTw6RAshNU3FSz3JHlifb6wDBlyIY7zGpZ+dJE
oxGJl+5MFKi5zE/ZDTg/fPa5dPNhP8X6nevFmD3dqWTuPsxZfx3Z/gJWGvNBmwwG
2r+cgw3oUh+6XLoBb+4U0yoehwI+kMXlrhD3wuSx8SOiuAc+23Jy2zImZ7EhrQxw
PhnwPlh06adThWU7g6IAt4cfT/632UbxbiSe0lyn1EQUIsiWM7pCOLya7KP0FEh8
o3mIKxxLDU25BJUeKxRP2oFleJ3rPUujvc6D4kYllwEl1uuw9E1tfQgFBCtYhfjC
KBbnQMp3tNgMT+cydBwhwSO3F0hIEyNiCk5OxCXiTprgpZSI5xCfS58bilSla3Dd
/Zg+use5DKQB6wLIvkAcygloLdpblB2U50+UBuh3HjLgg2cdtaQn0fmWPhM8hbRB

(continued)

Fig **9.8**   Encrypted, Signed Copy of config.txt

```
PERqOAFMqT2FDB2M2TNOkWubF/RumDrD+cy1m0ZmXg+caUCWrfTXCzjZG0Zki6fg
bBM16d0krNCXFPALDhEo41M366vUjWom38TK0dxwH/k430nR25deD1DDHoakULcp
rF+DEBPoXpo/P2H08V9tGWgDv3dLHGlHAcGV+YK9w8KDDgMle7vjmo5gz4Afib7N
J6JLaPqp2dUvkxCLKUwjubsdk7zfb4pMYfJqFngu309P8UE0sBQQ/TExo327yqQA
e/I7vPzd5E/cgAJv5c4jS0ltg3ifvxwGRDZ3G1lwp8sz7dApF59pInnHGvPZMwEj
srrSx7YU5EymmL/GbKAuNMs5/OLH0n0o8BoXmT0yfCZaXstrvOYKvhu09fQZ6/WI
QSO1wgJp8q0CgqE3fznB5FAICYQEb40D0vtdJ6seCkLXIsLmWOKmje28882m1Fnp
5nMPg9B+KdxtMPIDqogMb+138Qvun3AgiFcXiRf52zRB/sLzsFEATJZp7ccnRxor
vCQ63kWzTt7oN13gZHOyHLghHuf02w2MQjPitfO180psdNDNB7t141Z7DX/SAIV7
CfDzWLJYX1J4iVj1PHoBwc4iYoch0T1ZBQjIt5wnMS08XSoGLwGtklrsJP41qWnM
vgTzYvJDQw0rhT8s6kZiUo62dqikykPRpExWMyEl/pqegdG0XplnCxTio2m9CRBF
HJVZoCtS1JLOL1pRb1OIj1JC7c13rhs7JRUmB3QV5emTvWaDOnNsajW5pGsr2w==
=8vBP
-----END PGP MESSAGE-----
```

Fig 9.8   Encrypted, Signed Copy of config.txt *(continued)*

as the source cipher file and (1) decrypt it if it is encrypted and (2) check the signature if it is signed. By default, the output file has the same name as the input file with the .asc stripped off. Since we already have such a file, indicate another output name, such as config.copy.

We don't have to tell MacPGP which keys to use because the Key IDs of the keys involved accompany the message. In particular, temp's secret key is used in the decryption process and Moira's public key is used in the signature verification process.

MacPGP responds by asking you to enter the passphrase for your secret key (Figure 9.2); this is needed for the decryption. After you enter the passphrase "temp," MacPGP displays the following in the message window:

```
Enter pass phrase:
Pass phrase is good.  Just a moment......
File has signature.  Public key is required to check signature.
Good signature from user "Moira McIntosh <mm@apple.net>".
Signature made 1994/08/10 18:59 GMT

Plaintext filename: Macintosh HD:MacPGP Folder:config.copy
```

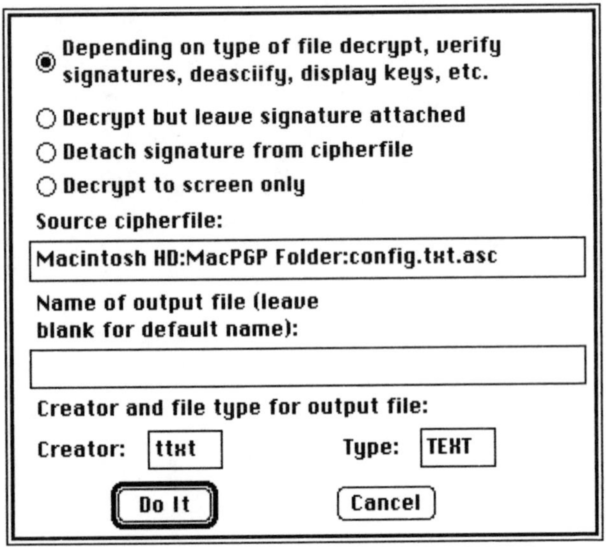

```
  ⦿  Depending on type of file decrypt, verify
      signatures, deasciify, display keys, etc.
  ○  Decrypt but leave signature attached
  ○  Detach signature from cipherfile
  ○  Decrypt to screen only
  Source cipherfile:
  ┌─────────────────────────────────────────────┐
  │ Macintosh HD:MacPGP Folder:config.txt.asc     │
  └─────────────────────────────────────────────┘
  Name of output file (leave
  blank for default name):
  ┌─────────────────────────────────────────────┐
  │                                               │
  └─────────────────────────────────────────────┘
  Creator and file type for output file:
  Creator: │ttxt│          Type: │TEXT│

      ╭──────────╮          ╭──────────╮
      │   Do It   │          │  Cancel  │
      ╰──────────╯          ╰──────────╯
```

Fig **9.9**   Decrypt Window

    The resulting output is stored in file `config.copy`. If you
check this against the original input from `config.txt`, the two
should be identical.

9.7 ADDING KEYS TO YOUR PUBLIC KEY RING

Now that you have seen that MacPGP works, it is time to add
some public keys to your key ring so that you can correspond
with others. First, we might as well dispense with the temp key.
Select the Remove Key option from the Key menu, then select `pubring.pgp`. MacPGP displays your public key in a window similar to Figure 9.6, but asking you to select a key for
removal. Select the key temp. MacPGP then asks if you are sure
that you want to remove this key. Respond "yes" and MacPGP
removes the key. MacPGP then tells you that the corresponding
secret key is present on `secring.pgp` and asks if you want to
remove that as well. Respond with a yes and MacPGP removes the
secret key.

Now we are ready to add some "real" keys to your public key ring. A good place to start is the set of keys that come with the implementation. These are generally to be found in a file with the name `keys.asc`. The contents of this file depend on the implementation. For example, PGP 2.6 and MacPGP 2.6 include a set of keys for the developers, many of whom are from MIT.

Select the Add Keys option from the Key menu. MacPGP prompts you for the file name for the key or keys and then prompts you to select a public key ring. Select `keys.asc` and then `pubring.pgp`. MacPGP responds in the message window:

```
Looking for new keys...
pub    512/4D0C4EE1    1992/09/10    Jeffrey I. Schiller <jis@mit.edu>
pub    1024/0778338D   1993/09/17    Philip L. Dubois <dubois@csn.org>
pub    1024/FBBB8AB1   1994/05/07    Colin Plumb <colin@nyx.cs.du.edu>
pub    1024/C7A966DD   1993/05/21    Philip R. Zimmermann
                                         <prz@acm.org>
pub    709/C1B06AF1    1992/09/25    Derek Atkins
                                         <warlord@MIT.EDU>
pub    1024/8DE722D9   1992/07/22    Branko Lankester
                                         <branko@hacktic.nl>
pub    1024/9D997D47   1992/08/02    Peter Gutmann
                                         <pgut1@cs.aukuni.ac.nz>
pub    510/DC620423    1992/08/27    Jean-loup Gailly
                                         <jloup@chorus.fr>
pub    1024/28748E05   1992/09/06    Hugh A.J. Kennedy <70042.
                                         710@compuserve.com>

Checking signatures...
pub    512/4D0C4EE1    1992/09/10    Jeffrey I. Schiller <jis@mit.edu>
sig!       C7A966DD    1994/05/07    Philip R. Zimmermann
                                         <prz@acm.org>
pub    1024/0778338D   1993/09/17    Philip L. Dubois <dubois@csn.org>
sig!       C7A966DD    1993/10/19    Philip R. Zimmermann
                                         <prz@acm.org>
pub    1024/FBBB8AB1   1994/05/07    Colin Plumb <colin@nyx.cs.du.edu>

                                                 (continued)
```

```
sig!        C7A966DD     1994/05/07     Philip R. Zimmermann
                                            <prz@acm.org>
sig!        FBBB8AB1     1994/05/07     Colin Plumb <colin@nyx.cs.du.edu>
pub     1024/C7A966DD    1993/05/21     Philip R. Zimmermann
                                            <prz@acm.org>
sig!        C7A966DD     1994/05/07     Philip R. Zimmermann
                                            <prz@acm.org>
pub      709/C1B06AF1    1992/09/25       Derek Atkins <warlord@MIT.EDU>
sig!        C7A966DD     1994/05/07     Philip R. Zimmermann
                                            <prz@acm.org>
pub     1024/8DE722D9    1992/07/22     Branko Lankester
                                            <branko@hacktic.nl>
sig!        C7A966DD     1994/05/07     Philip R. Zimmermann
                                            <prz@acm.org>
sig!        8DE722D9     1993/11/06     Branko Lankester
                                            <branko@hacktic.nl>
pub     1024/9D997D47    1992/08/02     Peter Gutmann
                                            <pgut1@cs.aukuni.ac.nz>
sig!        C7A966DD     1994/02/06     Philip R. Zimmermann
                                            <prz@acm.org>

Keyfile contains:
   9 new key(s)
```

This shows that nine new keys have been added to your public key ring. MacPGP also shows the signatures that are attached to each of these public keys. The presence of a signature means that the signer is certifying that the signed key is valid: that is, the key is owned by the person identified by the associated User ID.

After listing the keys that have been entered, MacPGP alerts the user that one or more of the keys aren't fully certified. For a key to be fully certified, it must be signed by you or by someone you have designated to be trusted to sign keys. So far, you have not granted such trust to anyone, so the keys remain uncertified. For now, answer "No" to this question.

Let's see how we have done, by viewing the current contents of your public key ring. Select View Keyring from the Key menu.

MacPGP asks you to select a key ring. Then MacPGP displays the window of Figure 9.10. Using the scroll bar at the side of the window, you can scroll through your entire key ring. There are ten keys, including the user's. If you select the OK button, you will get a complete listing in the message window. If you want to see the signatures as well, then select the box labeled "Show signatures also" and then select OK. Then you get the following in the message window:

```
Key ring: 'Macintosh HD:MacPGP Folder:pubring.pgp'
Type   bits/keyID      Date          User ID
pub    512/4D0C4EE1    1992/09/10    Jeffrey I. Schiller <jis@mit.edu>
sig    C7A966DD                      Philip R. Zimmermann
                                        <prz@acm.org>
sig    8DCBB1C3                      (Unknown signator, can't be
                                        checked)
sig    71946BDF                      (Unknown signator, can't be
                                        checked)
sig    396D3B7                       (Unknown signator, can't be
                                        checked)
sig    8CB4B951                      (Unknown signator, can't be
                                        checked)
pub    1024/0778338D   1993/09/17    Philip L. Dubois <dubois@csn.org>
sig    C7A966DD                      Philip R. Zimmermann
                                        <prz@acm.org>
pub    1024/FBBB8AB1   1994/05/07    Colin Plumb <colin@nyx.cs.du.edu>
sig    C7A966DD                      Philip R. Zimmermann
                                        <prz@acm.org>
sig    865AA7F3                      (Unknown signator, can't be
                                        checked)
sig    FBBB8AB1                      Colin Plumb <colin@nyx.cs.du.edu>
pub    1024/C7A966DD   1993/05/21    Philip R. Zimmermann
                                        <prz@acm.org>
sig    C7A966DD                      Philip R. Zimmermann
                                        <prz@acm.org>
sig    FF67F70B                      (Unknown signator, can't be
                                        checked)
                                                       (continued)
```

```
pub     709/C1B06AF1   1992/09/25   Derek Atkins <warlord@MIT.EDU>
sig         C7A966DD                 Philip R. Zimmermann
                                        <prz@acm.org>
pub    1024/8DE722D9   1992/07/22   Branko Lankester
                                        <branko@hacktic.nl>
sig         C7A966DD                 Philip R. Zimmermann
                                        <prz@acm.org>
sig         8DE722D9                 Branko Lankester
                                        <branko@hacktic.nl>
pub    1024/9D997D47   1992/08/02   Peter Gutmann
                                        <pgut1@cs.aukuni.ac.nz>
sig         C7A966DD                 Philip R. Zimmermann
                                        <prz@acm.org>
pub     510/DC620423   1992/08/27   Jean-loup Gailly
                                        <jloup@chorus.fr>
pub    1024/28748E05   1992/09/06   Hugh A.J. Kennedy
                                        <70042.710@compuserve.com>
pub    1024/694C1FFD   1994/08/09   Moira McIntosh <mm@apple.net>
sig         694C1FFD                 Moira McIntosh <mm@apple.net>
10 matching keys found.
```

Here we see that some of the keys have been signed by "unknown signators." This simply means that you have no key on this ring for the Key IDs associated with these signatures.

9.8 VERIFYING MACPGP

So far, you have only been playing around with MacPGP on your own system. Before making serious use of MacPGP, you should verify that your version hasn't been tampered with in any way. It is conceivable that someone has introduced a virus that could damage your computer files or some sort of "back door" that allows them to defeat PGP's security. You an use the power of PGP to check your copy of MacPGP.

Every implementation of PGP comes with a signature of one of the developers. When PGP is shipped or posted to an ftp site, the developer signs the executable module of PGP. The signature

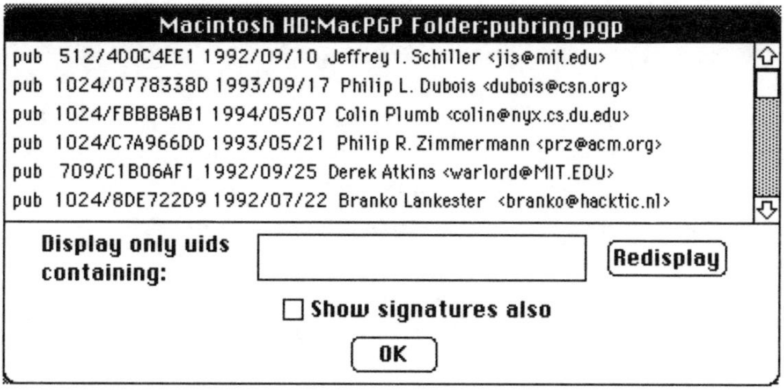

```
┌──────────────────────────────────────────────────────────────┐
│░░░░░░░░░░░ Macintosh HD:MacPGP Folder:pubring.pgp ░░░░░░░░░░░░│
├──────────────────────────────────────────────────────────────┤
│ pub  512/4D0C4EE1 1992/09/10 Jeffrey I. Schiller <jis@mit.edu>      ⇧│
│ pub  1024/0778338D 1993/09/17 Philip L. Dubois <dubois@csn.org>     ▓│
│ pub  1024/FBBB8AB1 1994/05/07 Colin Plumb <colin@nyx.cs.du.edu>     ▓│
│ pub  1024/C7A966DD 1993/05/21 Philip R. Zimmermann <prz@acm.org>    │
│ pub  709/C1B06AF1 1992/09/25 Derek Atkins <warlord@MIT.EDU>         │
│ pub  1024/8DE722D9 1992/07/22 Branko Lankester <branko@hacktic.nl>  ⇩│
├──────────────────────────────────────────────────────────────┤
│   Display only uids    ┌─────────────────────────┐  ┌──────────┐│
│   containing:          │                         │  │ Redisplay ││
│                        └─────────────────────────┘  └──────────┘│
│                        □ Show signatures also                  │
│                        ┌────────────┐                          │
│                        │     OK     │                          │
│                        └────────────┘                          │
└──────────────────────────────────────────────────────────────┘
```

Fig **9.10**   Key Viewing Window

is stored separately in a file with a name such as pgpsig.asc. Just as you can verify the signature of a message, you can verify the signature of your MacPGP execution module. If the signature is valid, this proves that your copy of MacPGP is from the genuine source and hasn't been altered.

There is a bit of a circular problem here: The executable file is signed with a developer's secret key (in this case Jeffrey I. Schiller) and you have obtained the developer's public key from the file keys.asc that came with MacPGP! So first you must somehow verify the developer's key. There are a number of ways of doing this, discussed in Chapter 6. One of the most efficient is by means of a key fingerprint. Let's get Jeffrey's key fingerprint from our public key ring. Select "Fingerprint key" from the Key menu. Following through the dialogue, you eventually get the response:

```
Key ring: 'Macintosh HD:MacPGP Folder:pubring.pgp', looking
for user ID "Jeffrey I. Schiller <jis@mit.edu>".
Type      bits/keyID      Date         User ID
pub     512/4D0C4EE1    1992/09/10     Jeffrey I. Schiller
                                       <jis@mit.edu>
Key fingerprint = BF 26 FA 39 50 04 5C BF 80 51 E3 52 4A 16 DF 96
1 matching key found.
```

A key fingerprint is simply a string of 32 hexadecimal digits that is, for all practical purposes, unique to a particular key (which is why it is called a fingerprint). The fingerprint that MacPGP displays is generated from the key that is actually on your public key ring. You can highlight this key using the mouse, copy it to the clipboard (ctrl-c), and then paste it into a Word or other word-processing document for printout. Now all you have to do is verify that key. To do this, you need to get the fingerprint from a separate source. In the case of MacPGP 2.6, the fingerprint is found in one of the documentation files that comes with the implementation. Of course, there is the risk that this also has been tampered with. Another possibility is to get another copy of the developer's key from a different source, such as a key server.

In any case, once you are satisfied that you have a valid public key, you can now verify the signature for this implementation. The exact sequence of steps you need to follow depends on the implementation; check the documentation that comes with your copy of MacPGP.

CHAPTER 10

Macintosh PGP
REFERENCE

Figure 10.1 illustrates the icons associated with the various MacPGP-related files. Clicking on any of these files starts MacPGP.

The MacPGP interface is built around the use of one window and five menus:

- PGP Messages Window: PGP messages
- Help: View/save/print help
- File: message/file processing
- Edit: cut/copy/paste
- Key: key management operations
- Options: configuration options

The Edit menu is inoperable except for the Copy command. We examine each of the other items in the preceding list in turn.

10.1 PGP MESSAGES WINDOW

When you open the MacPGP application, MacPGP displays the PGP Messages window. Initially, the window displays some copyright information and the current date/time on your system. It's a good idea to check that the date/time is accurate.

The PGP Messages window is only for output; you cannot enter data or commands into the window. Instead, as you perform

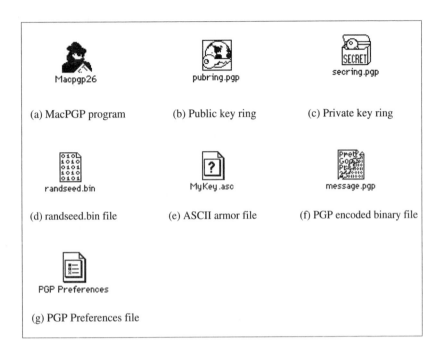

(a) MacPGP program

(b) Public key ring

(c) Private key ring

(d) randseed.bin file

(e) ASCII armor file

(f) PGP encoded binary file

(g) PGP Preferences file

Fig 10.1   MacPGP Icons

operations using the MacPGP menus, the messages window displays the commands and the results of the operations. For example, when you view a key ring, the key ring is displayed in the window. As with other Macintosh windows, the messages window has a scroll bar and its size can be adjusted.

Using the mouse, you can highlight any portion of the message window and then copy it on to the Clipboard, for later saving in a word processing application or to add to a PGP e-mail message. This is convenient for capturing fingerprints and listings of key rings.

10.2 HELP MENU

The help menu, which is actually part of the Apple menu, provides a way of getting on-line help and also of generating a MacPGP help file. Select Help from the Apple menu, and MacPGP displays

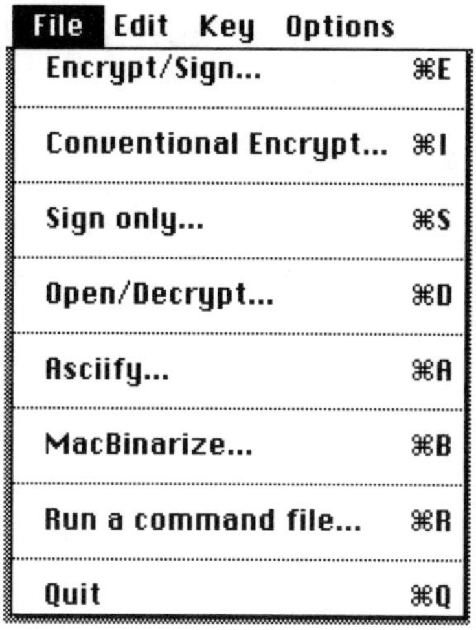

File	Edit	Key	Options

```
Encrypt/Sign...              ⌘E

Conventional Encrypt...      ⌘I

Sign only...                 ⌘S

Open/Decrypt...              ⌘D

Asciify...                   ⌘A

MacBinarize...               ⌘B

Run a command file...        ⌘R

Quit                         ⌘Q
```

Fig 10.2   The File Menu

a help window with a list of topics. You can scroll through the list and select any topic. In addition, the help portion of the Apple menu is activated, with the following options:

- Close Help: Closes the Help window.
- Save Help: Saves the Help documentation into a text file.
- Page Setup Help: Provides an expanded version of the standard page setup dialogue for specifying the format and layout of the printed Help manual.
- Print Help: Prints the Help manual.

10.3 FILE MENU

The file menu provides all of the PGP commands for processing files and messages for sending, receiving, and local encryption of files. Figure 10.2 shows the options available under this menu.

Encrypt/Sign

When you invoke this option, MacPGP steps you through a series of dialog windows to solicit the details of your request. First,

```
┌─────────────────────────────────────────────────────────┐
│        Macintosh HD:MacPGP Folder:pubring.pgp            │
├─────────────────────────────────────────────────────────┤
│ Double click on key to (un)select recipient(s):          │
├─────────────────────────────────────────────────────────┤
│  pub 1024/0778338D 1993/09/17 Philip L. Dubois <dubois@csn.org>     ⬆ │
│  pub  512/4D0C4EE1 1992/09/10 Jeffrey I. Schiller <jis@mit.edu>       │
│  pub 1024/FBBB8AB1 1994/05/07 Colin Plumb <colin@nyx.cs.du.edu>    ▓ │
│  ✓pub 1024/C7A966DD 1993/05/21 Philip R. Zimmermann <prz@acm.org>  ▓ │
│  ✓pub  709/C1B06AF1 1992/09/25 Derek Atkins <warlord@MIT.EDU>         │
│  pub 1024/8DE722D9 1992/07/22 Branko Lankester <branko@hacktic.nl>  ⬇ │
├─────────────────────────────────────────────────────────┤
│  Display only selections  ┌────────────────────┐ ┌──────────┐ │
│  and uids containing:      │                    │ │ Redisplay│ │
│                            └────────────────────┘ └──────────┘ │
│           ┌──────┐                      ┌────────┐              │
│           │  OK  │                      │ Cancel │              │
│           └──────┘                      └────────┘              │
└─────────────────────────────────────────────────────────┘
```

Fig 10.3 Key Selection

a file selection window comes up. It looks like a typical Macintosh
Open File window, except that it includes a Clipboard button,
enabling you to take input from the Clipboard. If you select the
Clipboard, the contents of the Clipboard will be encrypted and/or
signed and the results copied back onto the Clipboard. You can
then do a Paste operation to another application.

After you have selected a file or the Clipboard, MacPGP presents a key selection dialogue, an example of which is shown in
Figure 10.3. Select one or more recipients by double-clicking on the
corresponding keys; a check mark appears next to each selected
key. Please make sure to double-click; if you just click once, no
check mark will appear. If you have a large key ring, you can enter
a partial User ID or partial Key ID (prefixed with 0x) in the text
box labeled "Display only selections and uids containing:" and then
click on the Redisplay button. The display than shows only those
keys already selected plus those keys that have a User ID or Key
ID match with the string in the textbox.

You can get back to the overall display by blanking out the
text box and clicking on Redisplay again. By going back and forth
between the entire ring and a subset that matches the textbox
string, you can build up a list of selected keys. End the process by
clicking on the OK button.

SHORTCUT

If you use the Clipboard to provide input to the encryption function, you can specify the recipients on the first line as follows: Begin the first line on the Clipboard with To: and follow this, on the same line with one or more User ID strings separated by spaces. Then, MacPGP will not show the Key Selection window of Figure 10.3 but will instead use the To: line to identify the keys. MacPGP will encrypt the remainder of the Clipboard contents, after the first line.

After you have selected one or more recipients, MacPGP displays the command window shown in Figure 10.4. The upper left-hand portion displays the three alternative commands:

- Encrypt: The file Source file is encrypted using the public key[1] indicated by Recipient user_id.
- Sign only: The file Source file is signed using the secret key indicated by My user_id.
- Sign and Encrypt: Both of the preceding two operations are performed.

The upper right-hand portion lists command options:

- Use conventional encryption: Encrypts a file using only conventional encryption. In this case, MacPGP prompts you for a passphrase and use that passphrase to generate the encryption key. Later, to decrypt the file enter the usual decryption command; MacPGP prompts you for the passphrase. This option is only available for the Encrypt or Encrypt and Sign functions.
- Treat source file as text: Treat the input as an ASCII text file. When this option is present, MacPGP first converts the input to canonical form. Later, when the message is received on another system and the original file is recovered,

---

[1] The actual procedure is to use conventional encryption with a one-time session key and then to encrypt that session key with the recipient's public key and attach the result to the ciphertext; for convenience we simply say that the plaintext is encrypted using the recipient's public key.

```
┌─────────────────────────────────────────────────────────┐
│                                                           │
│                    ☐ Use conventional encryption          │
│    ○ Encrypt       ☒ Treat source file as text            │
│    ● Encrypt and sign   ☐ Create separate signature file  │
│    ○ Sign only     ☐ Only allow viewing by recipient      │
│                         Produce output in ASCII radix-64  │
│                    ☒ format                               │
│                         Treat source as a Macintosh file  │
│                    ☐ (MacBinarize before encrypting)      │
│    Source file:    ☐ Wipe out source file                 │
│  ┌──────────────────────────────────────────────────┐    │
│  │ Macintosh HD:MacPGP Folder:config.txt             │    │
│  └──────────────────────────────────────────────────┘    │
│  My user_id: ┌─────────────────────┐ ┌──────────────┐     │
│              │ Moira McIntosh      │ │Change my uid │     │
│              └─────────────────────┘ └──────────────┘     │
│  Recipient user_id: ┌──────────────────────────────┐      │
│                     │ Jeffrey I. Schiller           │      │
│                     └──────────────────────────────┘      │
│         ┌──────────┐              ┌──────────┐             │
│         │  Do It   │              │ Cancel   │             │
│         └──────────┘              └──────────┘             │
│                                                           │
└─────────────────────────────────────────────────────────┘
```

Fig 10.4   Encrypt/Sign File

the recipient's PGP converts from canonical form to the local text format. These conversions have to do primarily with the proper handling of carriage returns and line feeds, as explained in Chapter 4.

• Create separate signature file: The result is a signature in a file with the same base name as the signed file, but ending in .sig or .asc, depending on whether the ASCII armor option is selected. Later, when an attempt is made to decrypt this file, PGP prompts for the name of the file to which this signature refers. This option is only available for the Sign Only function.

• Only allow viewing by recipient: If a message is encrypted and/or signed with this option, then the recipient's PGP will not process the file and produce an output file. Instead, the recipient is told that the message is for display only and asked whether or not to display it now. PGP displays the message one screen at a time in the message window, in a manner similar to the UNIX more command. This option is only available for the Encrypt or Encrypt and Sign functions.

- Produce output in ASCII radix-64 format: This option causes MacPGP to convert the output to ASCII armor format, so that it can be sent via electronic mail. Without this option, part or all of the output will be raw binary data and may be corrupted or rejected by an e-mail facility.
- Treat source as a Macintosh file (MacBinarize before encrypting): This option is unique to the Macintosh version of PGP. The file system on Macintosh is quite different from that on most other operating systems. A Macintosh file structure includes either a data fork or a resource fork or both. The data fork contains file data that usually can be used on a different computer. The resource fork contains Macintosh-specific information, such as the type of file (document, application, INIT, etc.) and associated attributes (icon, time stamps, etc.); the resource fork also contains the executable code of an application. None of the resource fork information is usable on other systems. The MacBinary format facilitates transfer of files between Macintosh systems; in essence, MacBinary packages both the data and resource forks of a file into a single data fork with a header that acts as a packing slip describing the file. By default, MacPGP only encodes the data fork of a selected file. If you wish to send an encrypted and/or signed file to another Macintosh, the Treat Source as Macintosh option will first convert the file to MacBinary format and then perform the PGP processing. This option is mutually exclusive with the option, Treat Source File as Text.
- Wipe out source file: This option causes MacPGP to wipe out the original file so that only the ciphertext is retained.

The lower part of the command window shows the source file that you have selected and the User ID of the intended recipient. If there is more than one recipient, the User ID in the window is followed by three dots. The User ID for your secret key is also shown. If you have more than one key on your secret key ring, MacPGP selects the first key; you can change this by clicking on the "Change my uid" button.

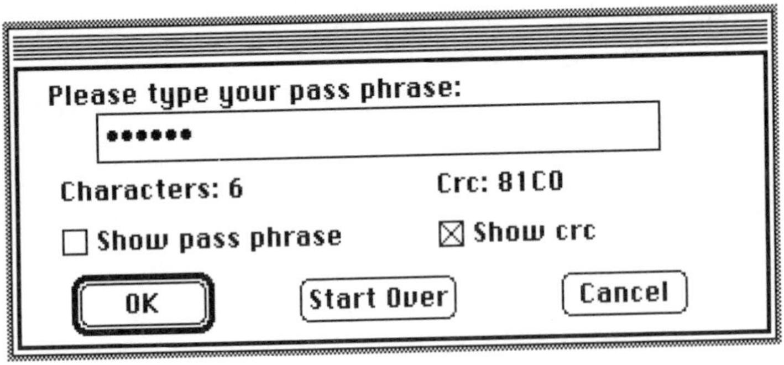

Please type your pass phrase:

    ••••••

Characters: 6   Crc: 81C0
☐ Show pass phrase   ☒ Show crc

[OK   ]   [Start Over]   [Cancel]

Fig 10.5   Passphrase Window

If you select either the "Encrypt and Sign" or the "Sign
Only" option, then after you click the Do It button (Figure 10.4),
MacPGP asks you for your passphrase using the window of Figure
10.5. This window includes the following elements:

- Text box for your passphrase: as you type your passphrase
  a bullet appears for each letter, unless you indicate that
  the passphrase should be shown.
- Show Pass Phrase option: If this box is checked, you
  passphrase appears in the text box as you type it.
- Show crc: This is a 16-bit cyclic redundancy check, or
  checksum, that is displayed as four hexadecimal digits if
  this box is checked. The CRC is recalculated after each
  character is entered.

If you want to be able to check that you have entered the correct passphrase or partial passphrase without displaying it, the
CRC provides an alternative means. You must have previously
memorized the CRC to use this feature.

Conventional Encrypt

The Conventional Encryption selection under the File menu
provides the same functionality as the conventional encryption
option of the Encrypt/Sign File selection, plus some additional features. When you invoke this option, MacPGP first asks you to

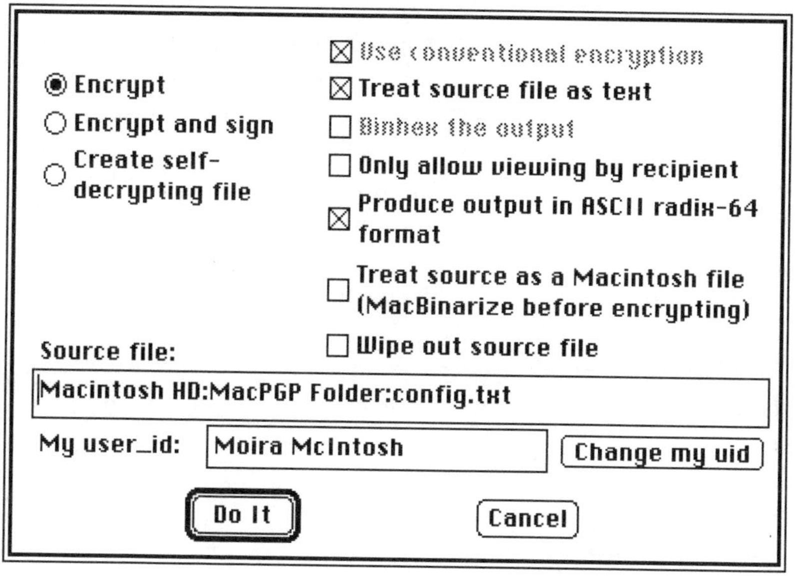

Fig 10.6   Conventional Encryption Command Window

select a file. Then MacPGP displays the command window shown
in Figure 10.6.

Note that this window is quite similar to Figure 10.4. It
doesn't include a recipient field, since no recipient's public key is
used. In the upper left-hand portion of the window, one new command is added: Create Self-Decrypting File. When this option is
selected, MacPGP encrypts the file with the passphrase you select,
adds the logic for the IDEA encryption algorithm, and then stores
it as an application. If you double-click on the application, the following steps are performed:

1. The application is invoked.
2. The user is prompted for a passphrase.
3. The file is decrypted using IDEA.
4. The application shows a file name and asks if it is OK to
   save the plaintext in that file.

There are some changes in the list of command options as well.

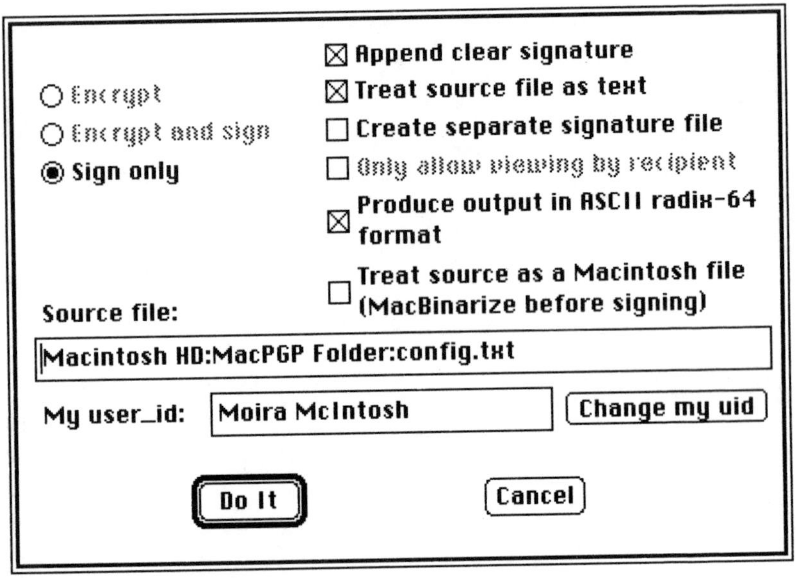

```
                  ☒ Append clear signature
  ○ Encrypt       ☒ Treat source file as text
  ○ Encrypt and sign  ☐ Create separate signature file
  ⦿ Sign only     ☐ Only allow viewing by recipient
                  ☒ Produce output in ASCII radix-64
                     format
                  ☐ Treat source as a Macintosh file
  Source file:       (MacBinarize before signing)

  ┌────────────────────────────────────────────────┐
  │Macintosh HD:MacPGP Folder:config.txt           │
  └────────────────────────────────────────────────┘

  My user_id:  ┌──────────────────────┐  ┌Change my uid┐
               │Moira McIntosh        │  └─────────────┘
               └──────────────────────┘

          ┌ Do It ┐          ┌Cancel┐
          └───────┘          └──────┘
```

Fig 10.7   Sign Only Command Window

The box for Use Conventional Encryption is automatically checked and cannot be unchecked. The new option, Binhex the Output, is available for use with self-decrypting files. BinHex is a conversion algorithm similar in intent to ASCII armor. A self-decrypting file saved in BinHex can be transferred to another Macintosh machine by e-mail, converted back to binary form, and then launched as an application for decrypting on that target machine. The primary purpose of the BinHex option is to send encrypted files to a Macintosh user who does not use MacPGP. However, the target user needs the passphrase in order to decrypt the file.

Sign Only

The Sign Only selection under the File menu provides the same functionality as the Sign Only option of the Encrypt/Sign File selection, plus one additional feature. When you invoke this option, MacPGP first asks you to select a file. Then MacPGP displays the command window shown in Figure 10.7.

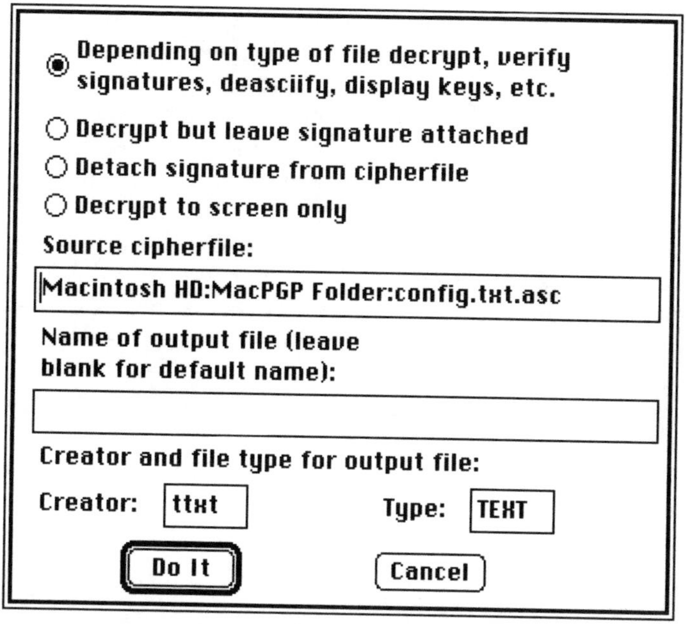

○ **Depending on type of file decrypt, verify signatures, deasciify, display keys, etc.**
○ Decrypt but leave signature attached
○ Detach signature from cipherfile
○ Decrypt to screen only
Source cipherfile:

Macintosh HD:MacPGP Folder:config.txt.asc

Name of output file (leave
blank for default name):

Creator and file type for output file:
Creator: ttxt   Type: TEXT

Do It   Cancel

Fig 10.8   Decrypt File

Note that this window is quite similar to Figure 10.4. It doesn't include a recipient field, since no recipient's public key is used. The Sign only command is automatically checked and cannot be unchecked. The new command option is Append Clear Signature; this option can only be selected if the Treat Source File as Text option is also selected. When this option is selected, the resulting text file can be displayed without using PGP and can therefore be read by anyone. However, the message is signed, assuring its authenticity.

Open/Decrypt

When you invoke this option, MacPGP first asks you to select a file. Then MacPGP displays the command window shown in Figure 10.8. The upper left-hand portion displays the four alternative commands, which we examine in turn.

Process Any File MacPGP first checks to see if the file is in ASCII armor format. If so, MacPGP removes the ASCII armor. When MacPGP prepares a message with ASCII armor, if the size of the output exceeds the limit specified in the configuration parameter ArmorLines (see Section 10.5 discussion of the Options Menu), MacPGP produces a sequence of output files with suffixes .as1, .as2, and so on. When the recipient issues the decryption command and selects file.as1, PGP automatically looks for file.as2, file.as3, etc., and processes the merged file.

If the file is encrypted using public-key encryption to encrypt the session key, the file includes the Key ID of the public key that was used in the encryption process. MacPGP searches the user's secring.pgp for the matching secret key. If that key isn't present, MacPGP prints out a warning message. Otherwise, MacPGP prompts the user for the passphrase of the secret key and decrypts the file.

If the file is conventionally encrypted, MacPGP prompts the user for the passphrase and decrypts the file.

If the file is signed, it includes the Key ID of the public key of the signer. MacPGP searches the user's pubring.pgp for the public key. If that key isn't present, MacPGP prints out a warning. Otherwise, MacPGP verifies that the signature is valid and removes the signature.

The output from the decryption and/or signature processing is stored in a new file with the following naming conventions. If the old file ends in .asc or .pgp, then the new file has the same name without the .asc or .pgp. Otherwise, the new file has the same name as the old file and MacPGP asks whether you want to overwrite. You can specify the name of the output file in the command window.

Decrypt But Leave Signature Attached This command allows you to decrypt a message but leave the signature attached to it. This enables you or anyone else to determine at a later time the validity of the file.

Detach Signature from Cipherfile If you have a file that includes an attached signature, this command create two new files: One consists of the plaintext file without the signature, and the other consists of the detached signature. The detached signature will be in a file with a name of the form filename.sig.

Decrypt to Screen Only   Even if the sender hasn't used the option to allow viewing only by recipient, the recipient can force a similar behavior by using this command. In this case, MacPGP automatically displays its output one screen at a time in the message window. At the end, the user is asked whether or not to save the output permanently.

Asciify

When this command is issued, MacPGP prompts you to select a file. MacPGP then produces a file, ending in .asc, with ASCII armor but without a signature and without encryption. Thus MacPGP provides a handy way of protecting a file for e-mail transmission even though security services aren't needed. Anyone with PGP can de-armor it without difficulty by issuing the decrypt command. In addition, for long files, this command conveniently produces a multi-part file for transmission.

MacBinarize

This command converts a file to MacBinary format[2]. The primary purpose of this command is for verification of detached signatures on executable Macintosh programs. In particular, this command is used for the verification of detached signatures on MacPGP itself. The steps one should take are:

1. Make a copy of MacPGP while MacPGP is not running.
2. Open the original MacPGP application.
3. MacBinarize the copy of MacPGP.
4. Select the detached signature.
5. When prompted for the associated file choose the MacBinarized file of step 3.

---

[2] See the discussion of MacBinary under the Treat Source as Macintosh option of the Encrypt/Sign command.

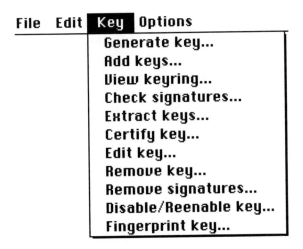

Fig 10.9 The Key Menu

Run a Command File

This command enables users to access all the commands and options supported by PGP, even those not visible through the MacPGP interface. A command file consists of a series of PGP command lines in the same format as for DOS PGP. MacPGP will execute these commands in a batch mode. This feature can be used for scripting a lengthy series of PGP operations.

When you select this command, MacPGP displays the following dire warning: "This function is an untested and unsupported kludge! Run this at your own risk!! Be sure to RTFM!!!" A word to the wise. . .

Quit

This command quits MacPGP.

10.4 KEY MENU

The key menu provides all the PGP commands for key management. Figure 10.9 shows the options available under this menu.

```
┌─────────────────────────────────────────────────────┐
│  Pick your RSA key size:                              │
│      ○ 512 bits- Low commercial grade, fast           │
│                  but less secure                      │
│      ○ 768 bits- High commercial grade,               │
│                  medium speed, good security          │
│      ○ 1024 bits- Military grade, very slow,          │
│                   highest security                    │
│        Pick your own size (between 384 and            │
│        1024 bits): │           │                      │
│  Number of bits in encryption exponent:  │ 17      │  │
│  User ID for your public key. Desired form is name    │
│  followed by E-mail address in angle brackets.        │
│  Eg: John Q. Smith <12345.6789@compuserve.com>        │
│  ┌─────────────────────────────────────────────────┐ │
│  └─────────────────────────────────────────────────┘ │
│        ┌──────────┐          ┌──────────┐             │
│        │    OK    │          │  Cancel  │             │
│        └──────────┘          └──────────┘             │
└─────────────────────────────────────────────────────┘
```

Fig 10.10   Key Generation

Generate Key

Figure 10.10 shows the key generation dialogue. Select a key size and a User ID. You may also select a public key exponent size (see Chapter 5). MacPGP places a new secret key on your secret key ring and the matching public key on your public key ring. You may have multiple secret keys on your secret key ring, so long as each one has a unique User ID.

Add Keys

When you select this command, MacPGP prompts you for the filename for the new key or keys and then for the file name of your public key ring. MacPGP then copies all of the keys from the key file to your key ring. If you add a key that already exists, and the keyfile copy contains new User IDs or new signatures, then those new User IDs or signatures are added to the existing key on the

```
┌──────────────────────────────────────────────────────┐
│         Macintosh HD:MacPGP Folder:pubring.pgp         │
├────────────────────────────────────────────────────┬─┤
│ pub  709/C1B06AF1 1992/09/25  Derek Atkins <warlord@MIT.EDU>     │⇧│
│ pub@ 1024/8DE722D9 1992/07/22  Branko Lankester  <branko@hacktic.nl> │ │
│ pub  1024/9D997D47 1992/08/02  Peter Gutmann <pgut1@cs.aukuni.ac.nz> │ │
│ pub  510/DC620423 1992/08/27  Jean-loup Gailly <jloup@chorus.fr> │ │
│ pub  1024/28748E05 1992/09/06  Hugh A.J. Kennedy <70042.710@compuserve.com> │ │
│ pub  1024/694C1FFD 1994/08/09  Moira McIntosh <mm@apple.net> │⬇│
├────────────────────────────────────────────────────┴─┤
│  Display only uids  ┌────────────────────────┐  ┌─────────┐ │
│  containing:        │                        │  │Redisplay│ │
│                     └────────────────────────┘  └─────────┘ │
│                  ☐ Show signatures also                │
│                   ┌──────────────┐                     │
│                   │      OK      │                     │
│                   └──────────────┘                     │
└──────────────────────────────────────────────────────┘
```

Fig 10.11 Key Viewing

key ring. After the key or keys are added, if any of the new keys aren't fully certified, you are asked if you want to certify any of the keys and, if so, you are also asked to assign a level of owner trust.

View Keyring

When you select the View Keyring command, MacPGP prompts you to select a public or secret key ring and then presents a display like Figure 10.11. The window shows the key length in bits, the Key ID, the date of creation, and the User ID or IDs for each key. You can scroll through the list of keys in the window.

If you enter a character string in the box labeled "Display only uids containing" and then click on Redisplay, only the key or keys that match that User ID are displayed. It isn't necessary to enter the entire User ID. If a partial User ID is entered, MacPGP does a search to match that string. For example, in Moira McIntosh's key ring (Chapter 9), the string prz will select Phil Zimmermann's key. A key can also be selected on the basis of Key ID. The convention is to enter a zero followed by the letter x followed by part or all of the Key ID. For example, the string 0x7A9 will select Phil Zimmermann's key.

If you click on the OK button, MacPGP provides a listing of this key ring in the message window. If you first select "Show signatures also," MacPGP lists all keys and their signatures in the message window.

Check Signatures

When you select this command and then select a key ring, MacPGP responds with a display similar to Figure 10.11, except that the box "Show signatures also" is replaced by the box "Only check trust levels."

This command causes MacPGP to do a complete pass through your public key ring. Each signature is checked to see if the signer's key is on the ring and if so, the OwnerTrust value assigned to the key owner is copied into the SigTrust value for the corresponding signature. Then, MacPGP recalculates the Validity for each key. In addition, if the user has defined a backup secret key ring in the `config.txt` file (see Section 8.4), then MacPGP checks the user's public key against the secret key on the backup file. MacPGP also produces two listings in the message window. First, MacPGP lists the selected key or entire ring, showing all signatures. Then, MacPGP repeats the listing, this time showing the trust level of each User ID (both for keys and for signatures) and the validity of each key.

If you select "Only check trust levels," MacPGP displays each key on the public key ring that is ultimately trusted (each of your public keys) and a signature chain for each of these keys. That is, MacPGP shows which keys are signed by the ultimately trusted key, and then which keys are signed by the keys signed by the ultimately trusted key, and so on.

Extract Keys

When this command is issued, MacPGP first displays a window that asks you to select a key ring. Once you have selected a key ring, MacPGP then responds with a display similar to Figure 10.11, except that the box "Show signatures also" is replaced by the box "Asciify the output." Next, you are presented with a file selection window that is similar to a Save As window in other applications. You can navigate to a particular folder and then enter a file name. MacPGP copies one or more keys and their signatures from you key ring into a key file. Note that you can select multiple keys by double-clicking on each selection. You should always use the "Asciify the output" option, which puts the file in ASCII armor format, so the result can be sent to others via e-mail.

EXTRACTING KEYS TO THE CLIPBOARD

If you have checked "Asciify the output" and then enter the name "Clipboard" in the file selection textbox, MacPGP places the ASCII-armored keys in the Clipboard rather than storing to a file.

Certify Key

You can sign the Key-ID/User-ID combination of any key on a public key ring, including your own public key, using this command.

Edit Key

The interpretation of this command depends on the key selected. When you invoke this command and select a public key ring, MacPGP displays a window similar to Figure 10.3, asking you to select a key for editing.

If you select your own public key, then you are prompted to add a new User ID to this key; the old User ID is retained. Whether or not you add a new User ID, MacPGP then asks you if you wish to change the passphrase for the corresponding secret key.

If you select someone else's public key, then MacPGP prompts you to select a trust level for the owner of this key.

Remove Key

When you attempt to remove a key with this command and the key has more than one ID, MacPGP asks you if you want to remove the whole key. If not, MacPGP asks you about each User ID separately. If you remove your own key from the public key ring, MacPGP asks you whether you also want to remove the matching secret key.

Remove Signatures

You can use this command to get rid of unknown or unwanted signatures, in order to clean up your public key ring. MacPGP prompts you one signature at a time for removal.

Disable/Reenable Key

The interpretation of this command depends on the key selected. When you invoke this command and select a public key ring, MacPGP displays a window similar to Figure 10.3, asking you to select a key.

If you select your own public key, MacPGP asks you if you wish to revoke this key. If so, your public key remains in your public key ring, but is designated as revoked. You can extract the revoked key to create a revocation certificate that can be sent to others

If you select someone else's public key , and the key is currently enabled, MacPGP temporarily disables the key. The key remains on the ring but cannot be used in encrypting messages. An @ symbol appears next to the key to indicate that it is disabled (e.g., Branko Lankester's key in Figure 10.11). At a later time, this command can be used to reenable the key.

Fingerprint Key

This command displays the fingerprint of the selected key in the message window.

10.5 OPTIONS MENU

The Options menu enables you to tailor the operation of MacPGP. Figure 10.12 shows the options available under this menu.

Set Keyring

For many operations MacPGP automatically selects the key that it needs from the default public or secret keyring. Normally, the files pubring.pgp and secring.pgp in the same folder as the MacPGP application are the default rings. The Set Keyring com-

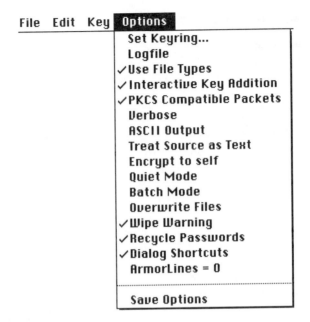

Fig 10.12 The Options Menu

mand allows you to change the default for one or more of the
following:

- your public key ring: This feature is especially useful if
  you have many public keys from other people. You could
  organize a number of different public key rings based on
  the criteria of your choice, and then temporarily change the
  default public key ring from this option.
- your secret key ring: Although it is possible to store more
  than one secret key on the same secret key ring, MacPGP
  always display the User ID of the default secret key from
  the default secret key ring in signing windows (i.e.,
  Figure 10.6, Figure 10.7); you must then select the other
  secret key (with the Change my uid button) when you
  wish to use it. If you have two different secret keys that
  you use with some regularity, it may be more convenient
  to put them on different secret key rings and then tem-

porarily change the default secret key ring.

- your secondary public key ring: When MacPGP is doing an automatic search for a public key, it first looks in your default public key ring and then your secondary public key ring, if one exists. For example, with the Open/Decrypt Command from the File Menu, if the file to be processed is signed, MacPGP looks first on the default and next on the secondary public key ring for the signer's public key.

Logfile

If you select this option, you can name a file to be used to save all of the text output (the message window) while this option is selected. This is useful for getting a printout of your public and secret key rings.

Use File Types

This option is unique to the Macintosh version of PGP. When this flag is on, "choose file" dialogs only display files with appropriate file types. For example, if you choose Certify Key from the Key menu, MacPGP only shows you files that are public key rings. Since this option simplifies the task of navigating through your file hierarchy, it should be turned on.

Note, however, that a file is not given the correct file type unless it was created by MacPGP or otherwise already used by MacPGP. For example, if you download a public key ring from another system, it will initially show up without the proper file type.

Interactive Key Addition

By default, when you add the keys from a keyfile to your public key ring, MacPGP adds all keys from that file to your ring. If you first select the Interactive Key Addition option, MacPGP asks you, for each key in the file, whether you want to add that key to your ring.

This feature is useful when you obtain a key file with a number of keys on it. For example, every implementation of PGP comes with a keys.asc file with keys for the various developers. You may want to add one or two of these, such as Phil Zimmermann's key, but, for example, have no need for the key of Branko Lankester. If the key file is large, it is easier to reject keys one at a time via MacPGP prompt than to add all the keys and then remove the unwanted ones.

PKCS Compatible Packets

This option specifies that MacPGP should use formats for signatures, public keys, and other PGP data structures that conforms to Public Key Cryptography Standards. These formats are compatible with all versions of PGP from 2.3 onwards and with other security standards such as Privacy Enhanced Mail (PEM). You should always set this option.

Verbose

When this option is set, MacPGP describes its operations in great detail in the message window. Normally it is wise to leave this option off. However, you might find it interesting to turn the option on and then generate a temporary pair of keys, just to see the type of information provided under this option.

ASCII Output

When this parameter is on, MacPGP automatically produces ciphertext and keys in ASCII armor format, suitable for handling by e-mail facilities. This is equivalent to always using the asciify option. If most of your use of MacPGP is for e-mail, you should enable this parameter.

Treat Source as Text

This parameter is equivalent to the command option found in the Encrypt/Sign command window. Recall that this option tells MacPGP to treat the input as an ASCII text file. When this option is present, MacPGP first converts the input to canonical form. Later, when the message is received on another system and the original file is recovered, MacPGP converts from canonical form to the local text format. Primarily, these conversions have to do with the proper handling of carriage returns and line feeds, as explained in Chapter 4. If MacPGP detects that the file isn't text, then it doesn't attempt the conversion. If most of your use of MacPGP is for e-mail of text, then this option should be selected.

Encrypt to Self

When this option is selected MacPGP always includes your public key in the process of creating an encrypted file. That is, any time that a file is encrypted, MacPGP includes you as one of the recipients. The convenience of this option is that you don't need to keep a plaintext copy of a message that you sent. You can keep the ciphertext copy and decrypt it whenever you need access to the plaintext.

Quiet Mode

When this mode is set, MacPGP displays only the minimum amount of information for each operation.

Batch Mode

When this mode is set, MacPGP won't ask unnecessary questions or prompt for alternate file names. This mode is useful if you want to set up a batch execution of some PGP operations.

Overwrite Files

When MacPGP produces a file whose default file name is the same as that of another file in the folder containing the input file, it normally asks you whether to overwrite the existing file or to use a new file name. With this option set, MacPGP won't ask but will instead automatically overwrite the existing file. This feature is useful for non-interactive, or batch, operation of PGP.

Wipe Warning

When you check the Wipe Out Source File box in the Encrypt/Sign window (Figure 10.4), MacPGP erases the source file after processing. If the Wipe Warning parameter is set, MacPGP first presents a warning message and asks if you are sure you want to wipe the source file. If this parameter isn't set, MacPGP wipes the file without warning. If you don't encrypt to self and you might accidentally check the wipe box, then the prudent course is to enable this option.

Recycle Passwords

This convenient but dangerous option causes MacPGP to remember a passphrase that you enter. MacPGP retains that passphrase as long as the application is open and only erases it when you close the application. This is convenient if you are going to sign or decrypt many files. It is dangerous if you ever leave your computer running without quitting MacPGP and someone else has access to your machine.

Dialog Shortcuts

When you select this parameter, you are presented with the following options:

- Use Clipboard for Input
- Set Encrypt/Sign Defaults
- Set Conventional Encrypt Defaults
- Set Sign Only Defaults
- Set Decrypt Defaults
- Use Default Keyrings for Key Operations

All of these options have the effect of reducing the amount of dialog

Use Clipboard for Input   When you select this option, MacPGP takes input from the Clipboard instead of a file, and places the result back onto the Clipboard. This is convenient for using MacPGP while in another application, such as Microsoft Word. From Word, copy some text. Then switch to MacPGP and encrypt it. Then switch back to Word and paste the PGP message block into your word processing file.

Set Encrypt/Sign Defaults   When you select this option, MacPGP displays the Encrypt/Sign File window (Figure 10.4). Select and deselect the options in the upper part of the window to suit your needs and click Do It. From now on, when you choose the Encrypt/Sign option from the File menu, MacPGP skips this window.

Set Conventional Encrypt Defaults   When you select this option, MacPGP displays the Conventional Encrypt window (Figure 10.6). Select and deselect the options in the upper part of the window to suit your needs and click Do It. From now on, when you choose the Conventional Encrypt option from the File menu, MacPGP skips this window.

Set Sign Only Defaults   When you select this option, MacPGP displays the Sign Only window (Figure 10.7). Select and deselect the options in the upper part of the window to suit your needs and click Do It. From now on, when you choose the Sign Only option from the File menu, MacPGP skips this window.

Set Decrypt Defaults   When you select this option, MacPGP displays the Open/Decrypt window (Figure 10.8). Select and deselect the options in the upper part of the window to suit your needs and click Do It. From now on, when you choose the Open/Decrypt option from the File menu, MacPGP skips this window.

Use Default Keyrings For Key Operations   When you select this option, MacPGP automatically selects your default public key ring for operations requiring access to a public key. When this option is not on, MacPGP always asks you to select a particular key ring, even if there is only one possible key ring to select.

Armor Lines =

Some e-mail systems impose an upper limit on the size of messages that can be transported. By default, MacPGP produces output that is limited to 720 lines of ASCII text. If a larger file is produced, then MacPGP breaks it up into pieces labeled .as1, .as2, and so on. You can set this parameter to any number of lines. If you set this parameter to 0, MacPGP will not break up the file, no matter how big it is.

Save Options

If you select this option before quitting MacPGP, the program stores the options that are currently selected. Otherwise, any changes you make via the Options menu are valid only for the current use of MacPGP and will be lost when you close the application.

WARNING: CONFIG.TXT OVERRIDES OPTIONS

As with other implementations of PGP, such as DOS PGP, MacPGP uses the config.txt file, which contains certain configuration parameters. MacPGP never alters this file but only reads it; to make changes in config.txt, you must use an editor or word processor. The settings indicated by the Options menu are saved in the PGP Preferences file in the System folder. If you make changes in any of the options and then select Save Options, MacPGP updates the PGP Preferences file.

The following options in the MacPGP Options menu also appear as parameters in the config.txt file: Interactive Key Addition, PKCS Compatible Packets, Verbose, ASCII Output, Treat Source as Text, and Armor Lines. The config.txt file settings override the options menu settings. For example, the user may think that he or she has changed the Armor Lines from 720 to 0, but the next time that MacPGP is loaded find that this selection has been overridden and is still 720. To avoid this surprise, place a comment indicator, #, at the beginning of the appropriate lines in config.txt.

Windows PGP

$\mathbf{A}$s of the time of this writing there are no full-blown Windows implementations of PGP. Such an implementation could conceivably exploit the full power of the Windows interface, including drag-and-drop techniques for invoking PGP functions. However, there are a number of Windows front-ends, or shells, that make the use of DOS PGP easier and more intuitive. Essentially, all of these programs provide a graphical interface that presents options to the user so that the user doesn't have to remember all of the one-letter options of DOS PGP and so that the job of selecting files and keys is simplified.

In this chapter, we look at two popular Windows front ends for PGP: WinPGP and PGP WinFront. The two have markedly different look-and-feel characteristics. The style of WinPGP is one that will be familiar to users of other Windows applications; commands and operations are organized by drop-down menus that are used to bring up various windows. PGP WinFront is organized around a number of control panels; when any particular control panel is displayed, the user can see all of the functions and options in a particular category. Before using either of these programs, it is best to have a working knowledge of DOS PGP. Therefore, please go through the sequence of operations described in Chapter 7 (DOS PGP: Getting Started) before using any of the Windows front ends.

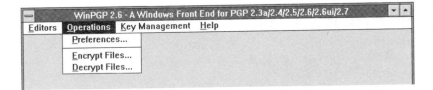

Fig **11.1**   WinPGP Main Window with Operations Menu

11.1 WinPGP

WinPGP is a shareware ($45) package developed by Christopher
Geib. It provides a menu-driven interface to PGP.

Main Screen

When you invoke WinPGP, it presents you with the screen
shown in Figure 11.1. This is a typical Windows application window, and includes four menus:

- Editors: Allows you to invoke either Notepad or Write as
  an editor for preparing input to PGP.
- Operations: Provides access to available PGP operations
  and to a facility for selecting preferences.
- Key Management: Provides access to key management
  operations.
- Help: Provides on-line access to PGP and WinPGP documentation. The documentation is brought up in the Write
  application, making it easy to search for key words and
  phrases.

Operations Menu

PGP operations other than key management operations are
controlled from this menu, as can be seen in Figure 11.1.

Preferences   When you select the Preferences option under
the Operations menu, WinPGP presents the window in Figure 11.2.
The following options may be toggled on and off:

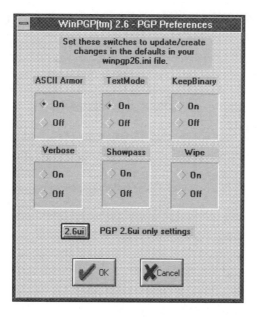

Fig **11.2**   WinPGP Preferences Window

- ASCII Armor: When this option is checked, PGP automatically formats the output of encryption and signing operations in ASCII armor format.
- Text Mode: Tells PGP to assume input is in text mode. This option is useful for transferring text files between different operating systems.
- KeepBinary: Preserves binary files and doesn't overwrite them with the encrypted output of PGP.
- Verbose: This is equivalent to the Verbose=2 option of PGP, which causes PGP to provide very detailed diagnostic and error messages.
- Showpass: When this options is selected, your passphrase is displayed on the screen whenever you enter it.
- Wipe: When this option is checked, PGP automatically wipes the input file when performing an encryption or signing operation.

The Preferences window also includes a button that is of use

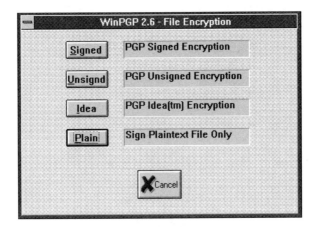

Fig **11.3**   WinPGP File Encryption Options

only for the 2.6ui version of PGP. When you are using this version and select this button, WinPGP present you with another dialog box that contains settings for `armor_version` and `version_byte`. Check the 2.6ui documentation to determine the setting for these switches.

Encrypt Files   When you select the Encrypt Files option under the Operations menu, WinPGP presents the window in Figure 11.3. There are four options:

- Signed: sign and encrypt a file.
- Unsigned: encrypt a file without signing.
- Idea: conventionally encrypt a file.
- Plain: Clear sign a plaintext file.

After you select one of these options, WinPGP presents you with another window to specify the details of the operation.

Figure 11.4 shows the window displayed for signed encryption. You can enter the path name for a file or select the browse button. In the latter case, WinPGP brings up a file selection window that is similar to that found in other Windows applications. Select a file and its pathname appears in the Filename field. Then

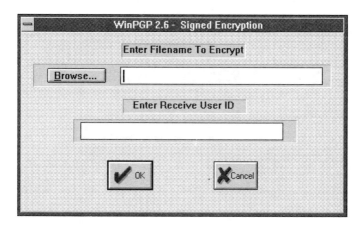

Fig **11.4**   WinPGP Encryption Window

enter one or more User IDs in the User ID field and select OK.
WinPGP then brings up PGP in a DOS window. The rest of the
operation proceeds in the same fashion as for DOS PGP.

For unsigned encryption, WinPGP displays essentially the
same window as that of Figure 11.4. Again, you need to enter a
filename and one or more User IDs. Again, WinPGP invokes a
DOS window running PGP to execute the command; in this case,
you aren't prompted for a passphrase.

For conventional encryption, WinPGP displays a window similar to that of Figure 11.4 but without the field for recipient User
IDs. Only a file name must be entered. When DOS PGP is invoked,
you are prompted for a passphrase for this encryption.

Finally, for clear signing, WinPGP displays essentially the
same window as for conventional encryption. Enter a file name
and PGP is invoked to prompt you for a passphrase and clear sign
the file.

Decrypt Files   When you select the Decrypt Files option
under the Operations menu, WinPGP presents a window similar
to the upper half of Figure 11.4. That is, you are asked to select a
file name, either by entering the path name or by using Browse to
specify the file in a file selection window. When you enter the

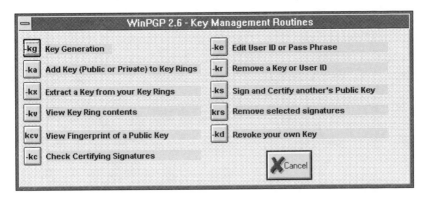

Fig **11.5**   WinPGP Key Management Routines

information and select OK, WinPGP invokes a DOS window running PGP to complete the operation.

Key Management Menu

PGP key management operations are selected by clicking on
the Key Management item on the menu bar. In response, WinPGP
displays the window of Figure 11.5. The following operations may
be selected:

- Key Generation: WinPGP invokes PGP to walk the user
  through the key generation process.
- Add Key: WinPGP displays a window that requests a file
  name, which may be entered directly or selected via the
  Browse button. Then PGP is invoked to complete the
  operation.
- Extract a Key: WinPGP presents a window that contains a
  field for entering the User ID or IDs to be extracted and a
  field to enter the file name to hold the extracted key.
- View Key Ring: WinPGP presents a window with a field for
  entering a User ID. If you leave this field blank, your entire
  public key ring is selected. WinPGP then invokes PGP,
  which displays the key or keys in the DOS window.
- View Fingerprint: WinPGP presents a window for entering
  a User Id and a window for optionally specifying a key ring

other than the default key ring. DOS PGP is then invoked
to display the fingerprint.

- Check Certifying signatures: This selection causes WinPGP
to invoke PGP to displays keys with their signatures.

- Edit User ID or Pass Phrase: WinPGP presents a window
that asks you to enter a User ID and optionally a key ring
other than the default key ring. DOS PGP is then invoked
to perform the operation.

- Remove a Key or User ID: WinPGP presents a window that
asks for a User ID, then drops into PGP to complete the
operation.

- Sign and Certify Another's Public Key: WinPGP presents a
window with fields to enter Their User ID and Your User
ID. If you leave the Your User ID field blank, WinPGP
assumes that you want to use your default secret key (first
key on your secret key ring). After you enter the required
information, WinPGP invokes DOS PGP to perform the
operation. In fact, the title of this option is somewhat mis-
leading. If you put your own User ID in the Their User ID
field and leave the Your User ID field blank, PGP is
invoked for you to sign your own key.

- Remove Selected Signatures: WinPGP presents a window
asking for the User ID of a key. Then PGP is invoked to
prompt you to remove or retain each of the signatures on
that key.

- Revoke Your Own Key: Again, this title is somewhat mis-
leading. WinPGP presents a window for you to enter a User
ID. If you enter your own User ID, PGP revokes it. If you
enter someone else's User ID, PGP will enable/disable it.

11.2 PGP WINFRONT

PGP WinFront (PWF) is a freeware package developed by Ross
Barclay. It provides a control-panel interface to PGP.

Main Screen

When you invoke PWF, it presents you with the screen shown
in Figure 11.6, which is divided into three parts:

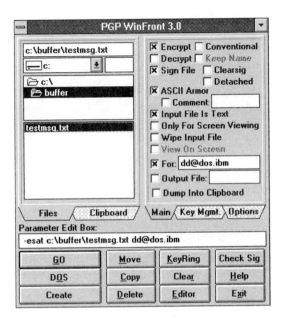

Fig **11.6**   PWF Main Screen

- Input Section: The upper left-hand portion of the screen is where you specify the input file to be used for a PGP operation.
- Operation Section: The upper right-hand portion of the screen lists the available PGP operations.
- Button Section: The lower portion of the screen presents a selection of PWF operations.

In addition, two other screens can be invoked from the main screen:

- Key Management Screen: When the Key Mgmt tab on the upper right-hand section of the main screen is selected, that section is replaced with a list of available PGP key management operations.
- Options Screen: When the Options tab on the upper right-hand section of the main screen is selected, the main screen is replaced with a screen used to select configuration options.

We now present a brief summary of each section.

Input Section

This section provides two ways to specify input to PGP. When the main screen is invoked, the Files tab at the bottom of this section is active (as in Figure 11.6) and the section displays drives, directories, and files in a manner similar to other Windows applications. You can select a file on any drive and can limit the display of files to just those that match a certain pattern (e.g., *.txt). In Figure 11.6, the user has selected the c: drive. In the buffer directory, the file testmsg.txt has been selected; the full pathname of this file is shown in the topmost field of the section. If you know the pathname of the file you want, you can enter it directly in this field rather than navigating through your directories and files to select it.

If you click on the Clipboard tab, the Input Section is replaced with a note telling you that input for any operation is from the clipboard. You can view the contents of the clipboard from this section by clicking the View Clipboard button. With the clipboard selected, when a PGP operation is invoked, WinFront automatically saves the contents of the clipboard to a text file and performs the operation on that file.

Operation Section

PGP operations other than key management operations are controlled from the main screen with the Main tab selected, as shown in Figure 11.6. The following operations and options may be selected:

- Encrypt: When this operation is checked, the Conventional option is active.
- Decrypt: When this operation is checked, the Keep Name option is active.
- Sign File: When this operation is checked, the Clearsig and Detached options are active, for clear signing and producing a detached signature, respectively.
- ASCII Armor: When this option is checked, the Comment option is activated. If the user checks the Comment option,

he or she may enter a one-line comment in the field to the
right of the Comment box.

- Input File is Text: Active if one or more of the following
  operations are checked: Encrypt, Sign File, ASCII armor.
- Only for Screen Viewing: Active only if the Encrypt opera-
  tion is checked.
- Wipe Input File: Active if one or more of the following operations are checked: Encrypt, Sign File, ASCII armor.
- View on Screen: Active if the Decrypt operation is checked.
- For: Active only if the Encrypt operation is checked; the
  user can enter the User ID of one or more recipients.
- Output File: Used to designate the file for output. If the
  user checks this box, a file selection window is displayed.
- Dump Into Clipboard: Only possible if the file to be dumped
  is a text file. Thus, the ASCII armor option must be selected for encryption or signing, and a decrypted file must produce text.

As options are checked and unchecked, the PGP command
that is built up is shown in DOS command-line form in the
Parameter Edit Box. For example, in Figure 11.6, the entries and
checkmarks in the Operations section produce the following pgp
command:

```
pgp -esat c:\buffer\testmsg.txt dd@dos.ibm
```

The user can subsequently make detailed modifications to the
command line by editing the line in the Parameter Edit Box.

Key Management Section

PGP key management operations are controlled from the main
screen with the Key Mgmt tab selected, as shown in Figure 11.7.
The figure also shows the result of selecting the Clipboard tab.

The following operations and options may be selected:

- Use Pages: This option causes PGP to display information
  one screen at a time; this is useful for viewing key rings.
- View Keys: View selected key or entire key ring. The
  KeyRing button may be used to select specific keys, or the

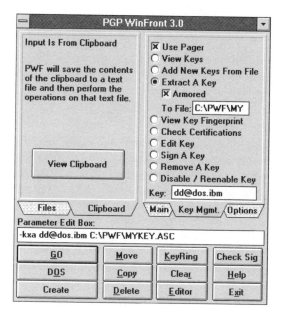

Fig **11.7**   PWF Key Management Screen

Key box, explained below.
* Add New Keys From File: The input file is the one designated in the input section of the screen (upper left-hand portion).
* Extract a Key: Extracts selected key in pgp or ASCII armored format. When the user clicks on the To File box, a file selection window is displayed; the user can then select an existing file name or enter a new file name.
* View Key Fingerprint: The fingerprint of the selected key is viewed in the PGP DOS screen.
* Check Certifications: The PGP certification operation is invoked to display keys, signatures, and trust levels in the PGP DOS screen.
* Edit Key: Edit selected key.
* Sign a Key: Sign selected key.
* Remove a Key: Remove selected key.
* Disable/Reeneable Key: Perform operation on selected key.
* Key: The user can identify a key by User ID or Key ID in this box.

All of the selections in this section that are indicated by a circle rather than a square are PGP operations. As the selections are made, a PGP command is built up in the Parameter Edit Box. For example, in Figure 11.7, the entries and checkmarks in the Operations section produce the following pgp command:

```
pgp -kxa dd@dos.ibm c:\PWF\MYKEY.ASC
```

The user can subsequently make detailed modifications to the command line by editing the line in the Parameter Edit Box.

Button Section

PWF operations, as opposed to PGP operations, are controlled from the panel of buttons at the bottom of the main screen, as shown in Figure 11.6 and 11.7. Each button can be invoked by mouse selection or by pressing ALT plus the underlined letter in the button label.

The buttons have the following interpretations:

- Go: Causes PWF to invoke PGP with the command specified in the Parameter Edit Box; this can be a command created from the Operations section or the Key Management section. This is exactly equivalent to entering "pgp" followed by the contents of the Parameter Edit Box, at a DOS prompt, PGP is invoked and the results of the operation are displayed on the DOS screen.
- DOS: Brings up a DOS screen and enables you to perform DOS commands.
- Create: When this button is selected, a file selection screen is displayed. After the user selects an existing file or enters a new file name, the default editor for PWF is invoked (e.g., Notepad or Write). The user can now create a message and save it in a file. PWF then resumes and the user has access to that file for encrypting/signing.
- Move: Allows the user to move the currently selected file (in the input section at the upper left-hand portion of the screen) to another directory or rename the file.
- Copy: Allows the user to copy the currently selected file to another directory.

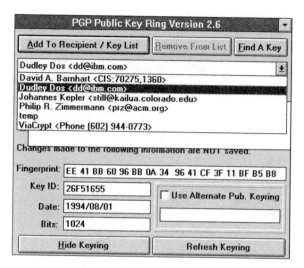

Fig **11.8**   PWF Key Ring Viewer

- Delete: Allows the user to delete the currently selected file.
- KeyRing: This loads the Key Ring viewer, discussed below.
- Clear: Deselects any options that have been selected in the current section (Operations section or Key Management section).
- Editor: Invokes the default editor.
- Check Sig: To use this button, the user first selects a file in the input section that contains a signature. When the button is selected PWF then displays a window asking for the selection of the file signed by this detached signature. Then, PGP is invoked to check the signature.
- Help: On-line help for both PGP and PWF.
- Exit: Exit program and save all settings. To exit without saving settings, use the control menu or press ALT-4.

Figure 11.8 shows the display that is generated when the KeyRing button is selected. The user can select a key from a key ring by scrolling through the ring and clicking on a key. The fingerprint, Key ID, date of creation, and key size are all displayed. If the user has selected the Encrypt option on the Operations section or one of the key management operations that can take multiple keys on the Key Management section, then the user can use the Add To Recipient/Key List button to select one or more keys to add to the argument list, and the Remove From List button to remove a previously selected key. The Find A Key button enables the user to search for a key that matches a particular User ID or Key ID substring.

At the bottom right-hand portion of the window is an area for designating and using an alternate public key ring. If the user clicks in the text box, PWF presents a selection window for entering the file name of an alternate public key ring. If the user subsequently checks the box Use Alternate Public Keyring, then PWF will display and use the alternate ring until the box is unchecked. This feature is useful for occasionally switching to a lesser-used key ring.

If new keys are added to the public key ring, they do not immediately show up in the key ring view of Figure 11.8. PWF maintains a buffer copy of the public key ring. To update that buffer, the user needs to select the Refresh Keyring button. Finally, the Hide Keyring button is used to close the key ring window and return to the main window.

Option Screen

The first time that you invoke PWF after installation, it begins with the options screen. Subsequently, you can recall that screen by selecting the Options tab on the main screen. Figure 11.9 shows the layout of the Options screen.

The options screen allows you to tailor the operation of PWF and to affect certain configuration parameters. The upper part of the screen consists of a number of fields that you may use to specify the following information:

- PGP Program: This contains the pathname to your PGP program. This can be in the form of a PGP.EXE or a PGP.PIF file. The .PIF file can be created by the .PIF Editor in Windows and is a technique for making DOS programs visible to Windows applications. The documentation for PWF recommends the use of the .PIF file.

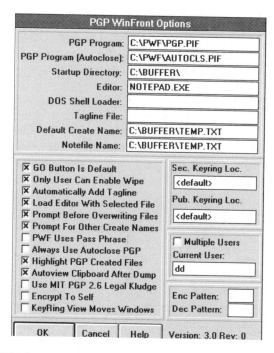

Fig **11.9**   PWF Options Screen

- PGP Program (Autoclose): This allows you to define a .PIF file for PGP with the Close Window on Exit option checked. WinPGP will use this .PIF for most PGP operations so that the PGP DOS window opens up only long enough to perform the desired operation and then closes. The non-autoclose .PIF file is used for decryption, when you will want to see what is going on after PGP exits.
- Startup Directory: This is the directory that PWF displays in the input section of the main screen on startup.
- Editor: This is the editor that will be invoked when the user selects the Create or Editor buttons.
- DOS Shell Loader: The name of command.com or .PIF file which invokes a DOS screen.
- Tagline File: This is similar to the .signature file used by Unix mail systems. It consists of one or more lines that

are automatically added to the end of any new file you create and typically is a name and e-mail address.

- Default Create Name: If you click on this box, you are presented with a file/directory selection window and can define a file name within any directory. PWF will then automatically use this file when the Create button is selected.

- Notefile Name: This allows you to define a file that will be used as a note file for making notes that can be easily referred to. The notefile is launched from the help button. This button presents a menu that includes PGP and PWF documentation as well as an option to load the Notefile.

In the lower left-hand portion of the options screen are a number of toggle options that can be set off or on:

- GO Button Is Default: Normally, the GO button on the Main and Key Management screens is highlighted, so that if you hit the enter key, the command in the Parameter Edit Box is highlighted. To avoid the accidental invocation of GO by inadvertently hitting the enter key, deselect this option.

- Only User Can Enable Wipe: If this option is selected, the PWF will not retain the Wipe Input File setting when the program is exited. It is safer to choose this option to avoid inadvertently wiping a file.

- Automatically Add Tagline: If this option is selected, PWF will automatically insert the contents of the Tagline file into any new file that you create from the Create button. If you don't select this option, then you will have to add the tagline manually by opening the tagline file. A good strategy is to select this option and then use the Create button for creating files that need the tagline and the Editor buton for files that don't.

- Load Editor with Selected File: When this option is selected, PWF will open the file selected in the input section when the Editor button is clicked. Otherwise, the editor is opened with no file. It is a good idea to select this option. If you want to use the Editor to create a new file (e.g., one without the tagline), make sure that no file is selected when you click the Editor button.

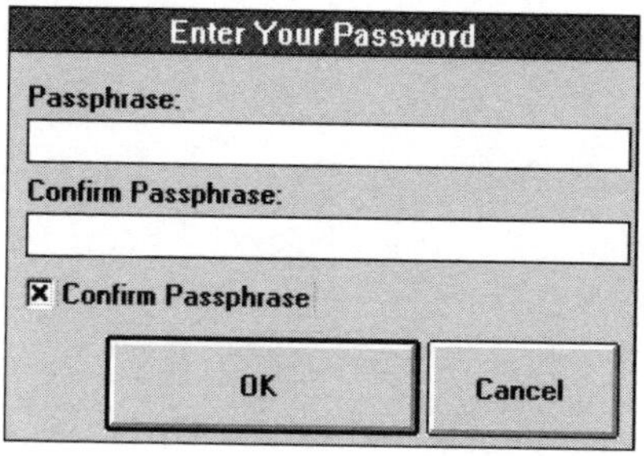

(a) With Confirmation

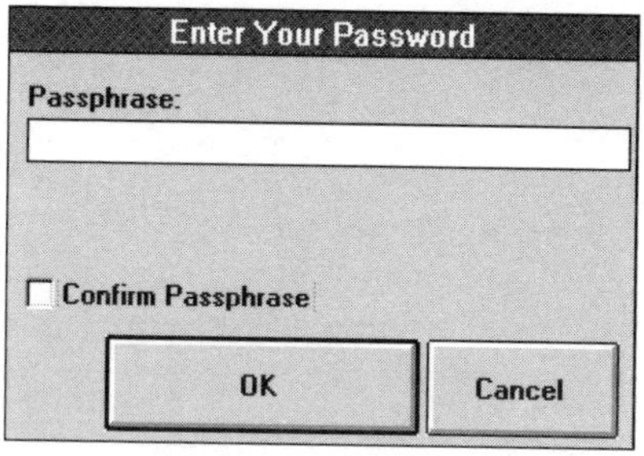

(b) Without Confirmation

Fig **11.10**   PWF Passphrase Prompt

- Prompt Before Overwriting Files: When you create a file, with this option selected, PWF will alert you if you are going to overwrite an existing file.
- Prompt for Other Create Names: When you create a file, with this option selected, PWF will ask you if you wish to use an alternate create file name.
- PWF Uses Pass Phrase: When this option is selected, one of the windows of Figure 11.10 appears when you open the PWF application. You then enter your passphrase once or twice (for confirmation) and PWF will always supply your password to PGP throughout a session. Otherwise, PGP will prompt you for your passphrase every time it is needed. The Confirm Passphrase box toggles between needing

to enter your passphrase once or twice; PWF remembers the setting of this toggle if you leave the program via the Exit button.

- Always Use Autoclose PGP: If this option is selected, PWF will always use AutoClose PGP even for the decryption operation.
- Highlight PGP Created Files: If this option is selected, when PGP creates a file, PWF will highlight (select) that file in the input section.
- Autoview Clipboard After Dump: If this option is set and if the Dump Into Clipboard option is set in the main menu, PWF will automatically bring up the clipboard whenever an operation is performed that dumps to the clipboard.
- Use MIT PGP 2.6 Legal Kludge: With this option selected, MIT PGP 2.6 will generate 2.3-compatible files rather than the newer format that is only readable by version 2.6 and later.
- Encrypt to Self: When this option is selected PWF always includes your public key in the process of creating an encrypted file. That is, any time that a file is encrypted, PWF includes you as one of the recipients. The convenience of this option is that you don't need to keep a plaintext copy of a message that you sent. You can keep the ciphertext copy and decrypt it whenever you need access to the plaintext.
- KeyRing View Moves Windows: If this option is selected, PWF adjusts the screen so that the main window is visible side-by-side with the key ring window.

To summarize the file options, if you select both Automatically Add Tagline and Load Editor With Selected Files, then these are your options:

1. To create a new file with a tagline, select the Create button.
2. To create a new file without a tagline, select the Editor button while no file is selected in the input section.
3. To open an existing file, select the Editor button while a file is selected in the input section.

To the right of the list of toggle options are two text boxes that can be used to designate the secret and public key ring locations. Initially, these locations are set to the PGP defaults; that is, secring.pgp and pubring.pgp in the same directory as PGP, respectively. This feature is useful if your principal public and secret key rings are located anywhere other than the default location, such as on a floppy disk.

If you have multiple secret keys, check the Multiple Users box and enter the User ID for the key you wish to use in the Current User field.

Below the multiple users section are two fields, Enc Pat and Dec Pat. These stand for encryption pattern and decryption pattern, respectively. If these fields contain patterns, PWF uses those patterns to form the suffix of file names for encryption and decryption. For example, you can set these to *.txt for encryption and *.asc for decryption.

P A R T 3

SUPPLEMENTAL INFORMATION

The Building Blocks
of PGP

T he cryptographic building
blocks of PGP are:

- Conventional encryption: IDEA
- Public-key encryption: RSA
- Secure hash functions: MD5

This chapter gives an overview of each of these algorithms.

12.1 CONVENTIONAL ENCRYPTION: IDEA

To get some feel for how conventional encryption works, we first
look at an easy example, the Caesar cipher. Next, this section
discusses DES and triple DES, which are two other widely-used
conventional encryption algorithms. It is useful to have some
understanding of these algorithms in assessing the strength of
IDEA. The section concludes with a description of IDEA.

Caesar Cipher

One of the earliest known and simplest conventional encryption schemes was used by Julius Caesar. The Caesar cipher
involves replacing each letter of the alphabet with the letter stand-
ing three places further down the alphabet, for example:

```
plain:     meet me after the toga party
cipher:    phhw ph diwhu wkh wrjd sduwb
```

Note that the alphabet is wrapped around, so that the letter following Z is A. We can define the transformation by exhaustively listing all possibilities:

```
plain:   a b c d e f g h i j k l m n o p q r s t u v w x y z
cipher:  D E F G H I J K L M N O P Q R S T U V W X Y Z A B C
```

A general Caesar cipher involves a shift of k letters, where k ranges from 1 through 25. If it is known that a given ciphertext is a Caesar cipher, then brute-force cryptanalysis is easily performed: simply try all 25 possible keys. Figure 12.1 shows the results of applying this strategy to the example ciphertext. In this case, the plaintext leaps out as occupying the third line.

Three important characteristics of this problem enabled us to use a brute-force attack:

1. The encryption and decryption algorithms are known.
2. There are only 25 keys to try.
3. The language of the plaintext is known and easily recognizable.

In most cases, we can assume that the algorithms are known. What generally makes brute-force attacks impractical is the use of an algorithm that employs a large number of possible keys. For example, the IDEA algorithm used in PGP makes use of a 128-bit key, giving a key space of 2^{128} or more than 3.4×10^{38} possible keys.

The third characteristic is also significant. If the language of the plaintext is unknown, then the plaintext output may not be recognizable. Furthermore, the input may be abbreviated or compressed in some fashion, again making recognition difficult. If a compressed file is encrypted, the plaintext may not be recognized when it is uncovered in a brute-force attack.

ROT-13

The Caesar cipher with a shift of 13 is actually in common use on the Internet. The function is called rot-13 (rot for rotation). By convention on the Internet and USENET, rot-13 is used to encode potentially offensive

KEY		PHHW PH DIWHU WKH WRJD SDUWB
	1	oggv og chvgt vjg vqic rctva
	2	nffu nf bgufs uif uphb qbsuz
	3	meet me after the toga party
	4	ldds ld zesdq sgd snfz ozqsx
	5	kccr kc ydrcp rfc rmey nyprw
	6	jbbq jb xcqbo qeb qldx mxoqv
	7	iaap ia wbpan pda pkcw lwnpu
	8	hzzo hz vaozm ocz ojbv kvmot
	9	gyyn gy uznyl nby niau julns
	10	fxxm fx tymxk max mhzt itkmr
	11	ewwl ew sxlwj lzw lgys hsjlq
	12	dvvk dv rwkvi kyv kfxr grikp
	13	cuuj cu qvjuh jxu jewq fqhjo
	14	btti bt puitg iwt idvp epgin
	15	assh as othsf hvs hcuo dofhm
	16	zrrg zr nsgre gur gbtn cnegl
	17	yqqf yq mrfqd ftq fasm bmdfk
	18	xppe xp lqepc esp ezrl alcej
	19	wood wo kpdob dro dyqk zkbdi
	20	vnnc vn jocna cqn cxpj yjach
	21	ummb um inbmz bpm bwoi xizbg
	22	tlla tl hmaly aol avnh whyaf
	23	skkz sk glzkx znk zumg vgxze
	24	rjjy rj fkyjw ymj ytlf ufwyd
	25	qiix qi ejxiv xli xske tevxc

Fig **12.1**   Brute-Force Cryptanalysis of Caesar Cipher

material or material that otherwise shouldn't be read without a warning (e.g., it gives away the ending of a book). Most USENET news readers include a command for decoding rot-13 text. In this case, we have a conventional encryption algorithm in which everyone knows the key ($k = 13$).

Table **12.1**

Noteworthy Conventional Encryption Algorithms

Algorithm	Year Introduced	Key size (bits)
DES	1976	56
Triple DES	1979	112
IDEA	1990	128

Let us now look at some of the most important conventional encryption algorithms, including IDEA (Table 12.1).

The Data Encryption Standard (DES)

The most widely used encryption scheme is defined in the data encryption standard (DES) adopted in 1977 by the National Bureau of Standards, now the National Institute of Standards and Technology (NIST), as Federal Information Processing Standard 46 (FIPS PUB 46). In 1994, NIST "reaffirmed" DES for federal use for another 5 years; NIST recommends the use of DES for applications other than the protection of classified information (e.g., financial and other business applications).

As with any encryption scheme, there are two inputs to the DES encryption function: the plaintext to be encrypted and the key. With DES, the plaintext must be 64 bits and the key 56 bits. Longer blocks of plaintext are encrypted in blocks of 64 bits.

In essence, DES processes plaintext by passing each 64-bit input through 16 iterations, producing an intermediate 64-bit value at the end of each iteration. Each iteration is essentially the same complex function that involves a permutation of the bits and substituting one bit pattern for another. The input at each stage consists of the output of the previous stage plus a permutation on the key bits, where the permutation is known as a subkey.

The process of decryption with DES is essentially the same as encryption: Use the ciphertext as input to the DES algorithm, but use the subkeys generated for each iteration in reverse order (i.e, use the 16th subkey for the first iteration, the 15th subkey for the second iteration, etc.).

The Strength of DES   Since DES was adopted as a federal standard, there have been lingering concerns about the level of security it provides. These concerns, by and large, fall into two areas: the nature of the algorithm and the key size.

For many years, the more important concern was the possibility of exploiting the characteristics of the DES algorithm to perform cryptanalysis. Because the design criteria for the algorithm have never been made public, there is a suspicion that the algorithm was constructed in such a way that cryptanalysis is possible for an opponent who knows its weaknesses. This assertion is tantalizing and over the years a number of regularities and unexpected behaviors in the algorithm have been discovered. However, no one so far has succeeded in discovering the supposed fatal weaknesses in DES. Indeed, as advances in cryptanalytic techniques have taken place, the underlying strength of the DES algorithm has become all the more apparent. As of this writing, no practical cryptanalysis attack method for DES has been published. Given that the algorithm has survived years of intensive scrutiny unscathed, it is probably safe to say that DES is one of the strongest encryption algorithms ever devised.

The more serious concern today is the key size. With a key length of 56 bits, there are 2^{56} possible keys, which is approximately 7.6×10^{10} keys. On the face of it, therefore, a brute-force attack appears impractical. Assuming that on average half the key space has to be searched, a single machine performing one DES encryption per microsecond would take more than a thousand years to break the cipher.

But the assumption of one encryption per microsecond is overly conservative. As far back as 1977, Whitfield Diffie and Martin Hellman, who were the first to describe public-key encryption in the open literature, postulated that the technology existed to build a parallel machine with 1 million encryption devices, each of which could perform one encryption per microsecond. The authors estimated that the cost would be about $20 million in 1977 dollars.

The most rigorous recent analysis of the problem was performed by Michael Wiener of Bell-Northern Research and is based on a known plaintext attack; that is, it is assumed that the attacker has at least one (plaintext, ciphertext) pair. Wiener takes care to provide the details of his design in his paper:

There have been numerous unverifiable claims about how fast the DES key space can be searched. To avoid adding to this list of questionable claims, a great deal of detail in the design of a key search machine is included in the appendices. This detailed work was done to obtain an accurate assessment of the cost of the machine and the time required to find a DES key. There are no plans to actually build such a machine.

Wiener reports on the design of a chip that uses pipelined techniques to achieve a key search rate of 50 million keys per second. Using 1993 costs, he designed a module that costs $100,000 and contains 5,760 key search chips. With this design, the following results are obtained:

Key Search Machine Unit Cost	Expected Search Time
$100,000	35 hours
$1,000,000	3.5 hours
$10,000,000	21 minutes

In addition, Wiener estimates a one-time development cost of about $500,000.

The Wiener design represents the culmination of years of concern about the security of DES and may in retrospect have been a turning point. The time has come to investigate alternatives for conventional encryption. Two of the most promising candidates for replacing DES are triple DES and IDEA.

Triple DES

Given the potential vulnerability of DES to a brute-force attack, there has been considerable interest in finding an alternative. One approach is to design a completely new algorithm, such as IDEA. Another approach, one that preserves the existing investment in software and equipment, is to use multiple encryption with DES and multiple keys.

The most popular form of multiple DES, referred to as triple DES, has gained a considerable measure of success. Triple DES uses two keys and three executions of the DES algorithm (Figure

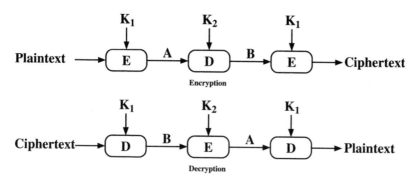

Fig **12.2**   Triple DES

12.2), with the function following an encrypt-decrypt-encrypt (EDE) sequence. There is no cryptographic significance to the use of decryption for the second stage. Its only advantage is that it allows users of triple DES to decrypt data encrypted by users of the older single DES; if the same key is used for all three stages, the effect is the same as a single stage.

Although only two keys are used, three executions of the DES algorithm are required. It turns out that there is a simple technique, known as a meet-in-the-middle attack, that would reduce a double DES system with two keys to the relative strength of ordinary single DES. With three iterations of the DES function, the effective key length is 112 bits.

International Data Encryption Algorithm (IDEA)

IDEA is a block-oriented conventional encryption algorithm developed in 1990 by Xuejia Lai and James Massey of the Swiss Federal Institute of Technology. It uses a 128-bit key to encrypt data in blocks of 64 bits. Figure 12.3 illustrates the process, in which each block is manipulated in eight rounds, or iterations, followed by a final transformation function. The algorithm breaks the input up into four 16-bit subblocks. Each of the iteration rounds takes four 16-bit subblocks as input and produces four 16-bit output blocks. The final transformation also produces four 16-bit blocks, which are concatenated to form the 64-bit ciphertext. Each of the iterations uses of six 16-bit subkeys, and the final transformation uses four subkeys, for a total of 52 subkeys. The right-hand

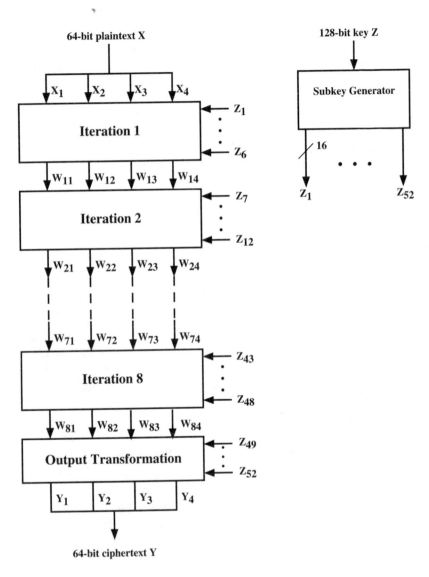

Fig **12.3**   IDEA

portion of Figure 12.3 indicates that these 52 subkeys are all generated from the original 128-bit key.

Each iteration of IDEA makes use of three different mathematical operations, each one performed on two 16-bit inputs to produce a single 16-bit output. The operations are

- Bit-by-bit exclusive, or
- Addition of integers modulo 2^{16} (modulo 65536), with inputs and outputs treated as unsigned 16-bit integers. That is, this function takes two 16-bit integers as input and produces a 16-bit sum; if there is overflow to a 17th bit, this is discarded
- Multiplication of integers modulo $2^{16} + 1$ (modulo 65537), with inputs and outputs treated as unsigned 16-bit integers, except that a block of all zeros is treated as representing 2^{16}.

The use of these three separate operations in combination provides for a complex transformation of the input, making cryptanalysis much more difficult than with an algorithm such as DES, which relies solely on simple bit-masking and permutation functions.

IDEA appears to have a number of advantages over DES or even triple DES. First, the key length of 128 bits makes it more resistant to brute-force key search attacks. Second, IDEA's internal structure appears make it more resistant to cryptanalysis than DES. Finally, IDEA was designed to facilitate both software and hardware implementations; for comparable implementations of IDEA and triple DES, IDEA should execute in much less time.

12.2 PUBLIC-KEY ENCRYPTION: RSA

One of the first public-key schemes was developed in 1977 by Ron Rivest, Adi Shamir, and Len Adleman at MIT. The RSA scheme has since reigned supreme as the only widely accepted and implemented approach to public-key encryption. RSA is a cipher in which the plaintext and ciphertext are integers between 0 and $(n - 1)$ for some n. For a long message, the message is broken up into blocks, with each block of size $\log_2 n$ bits.

Encryption and decryption make use of modular arithmetic;[1] for some plaintext block M and ciphertext block C with keys e and d:

---

[1] The expression $x \bmod y$ represents the remainder on division of x by y: the value of y is referred to as the *modulus* of the expression. For example, 131 mod 10=1 and 55 mod 7=6.

Key Generation

Select p, q p and q both prime

Calculate $n = p \times q$

Calculate $\phi(n) = (p - 1)(q - 1)$

Select integer e $\gcd(\phi(n), e) = 1; \ 1 < e < \phi(n)$

Calculate d $d = e^{-1} \bmod \phi(n)$

Public key $KU = \{e, n\}$

Private key $KR = \{d, n\}$

Encryption

Plaintext: $M < n$

Ciphertext: $C = M^e \ (\bmod \ n)$

Decryption

Ciphertext: C

Plaintext: $M = C^d \ (\bmod \ n)$

Fig **12.4**   The RSA Algorithm

$$C = M^e \bmod n$$
$$M = C^d \bmod n \ = (M^e)^d \bmod n \ = M^{ed} \bmod n$$

Both sender and receiver must know the value of n and e; only the receiver knows the value of d. Thus, this is a public-key encryption algorithm with a public key of $\{e, n\}$ and a private key of $\{d, n\}$. For this algorithm to be satisfactory for public-key encryption, the following requirements must be met:

1. Values of e, d, n exist such that $M = M^{ed} \bmod n$ for all $M < n$.

2. It is relatively easy to calculate M^e and C^d for all values of $M < n$.
3. It is infeasible to determine d given e and n.

The first two statements are true, and the third statement is true for a large values of e and n.

Figure 12.4 summarizes the RSA algorithm. Begin by selecting two prime numbers, p and q, and calculating their product n, which is the modulus for encryption and decryption. Next, we need the quantity $\phi(n)$, referred to as the *Euler totient* of n, which is the number of positive integers less than n and relatively prime[2] to n. It can be shown that $\phi(n) = (p - 1)(q - 1)$. Then select an integer e that is relatively prime to $\phi(n)$. Finally, calculate d as the multiplicative inverse[3] of e, modulo $\phi(n)$. It can be shown that d and e have the desired properties.

The private key consists of $\{d, n\}$ and the public key consists of $\{e, n\}$. Suppose that Alice has published her public key and that Bob wishes to send the message M to Alice. Then Bob calculates $C = M^e \pmod n$ and transmits C. Upon receipt of this ciphertext, Alice decrypts by calculating $M = C^d \pmod n$.

An example is shown in Figure 12.5. In this example the keys were generated as follows:

1. Select two prime numbers, $p = 7$ and $q = 17$.
2. Calculate $n = pq = 7 \times 17 = 119$.
3. Calculate $\phi(n) = (p-1)(q-1) = 96$.
4. Select e such that e is relatively prime to $\phi(n) = 96$ and less than $\phi(n)$; in this case $e = 5$.
5. Determine d such that $de = 1 \bmod 96$ and $d < 96$. The correct value is $d = 77$, because $77 \times 5 = 385 = 4 \times 96 + 1$.

The resulting keys are public key = $\{5, 119\}$ and private key = $\{77, 119\}$. The example shows the use of these keys for a plaintext

---

[2] Two numbers are relatively prime if they have no common factors exept 1. That is, there is no number other than 1 that divides each of the two numbers without a remainder.

[3] In modular arithmetic, the multiplicative inverse of x, modulo y, is a number z such that $(x \times z) \bmod y = 1$.

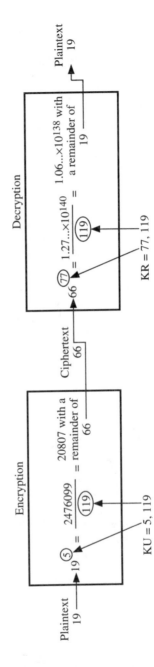

Fig 12.5   Example of RSA Algorithm

input of M = 19. For encryption, 19 is raised to the 5th power, yielding 2,476,099. Upon division by 119, the remainder is determined to be 66. Hence $19^5 \equiv 66 \bmod 119$, and the ciphertext is 66. For decryption, it is determined that $66^{77} \equiv 19 \bmod 119$.

NUMBER THEORY

An in-depth understanding of RSA and other public-key algorithms requires a basic knowledge of number theory. My book, Network and Internetwork Security (Prentice-Hall, 1995), contains a concise summary of those aspects of number theory pertinent to public-key encryption. In my opinion, by far the clearest and easiest to read treatment is in the book Invitation to Number Theory by Oystein Ore (available from the Mathematical Association of America, Washington DC). Even the severely math-phobic among you will find this book painless and even fun to read.

12.3 SECURE HASH FUNCTION: MD5

The MD5 message-digest algorithm was developed by Ron Rivest at MIT (the "R" in the RSA [Rivest-Shamir-Adelman] public-key encryption algorithm). The algorithm takes as input a message of arbitrary length and produces as output a 128-bit hash code. The input is processed in 512-bit blocks.

Figure 12.6 depicts the overall processing of a message to produce a digest.

- **Step 1: Append Padding Bits**

   The message is padded so that the length of the padded message is 64 bits less than an integer multiple of 512 bits. Padding is always added, even if the message is already of the desired length. For example, if the message is 448 bits long, it is padded by 512 bits to 960 bits. Thus the number of padding bits is in the range of 1 to 512. The padding consists of a single 1-bit followed by the necessary number of 0-bits.

- **Step 2: Append Length**

   A 64-bit representation of the length in bits of the original message (before padding) is appended to the result of

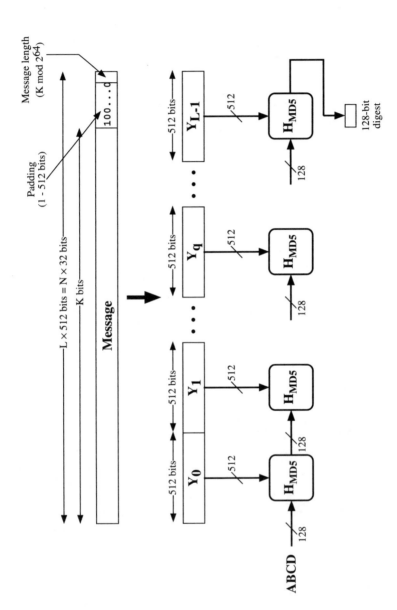

Fig **12.6** MD5

Step 1. If the original length is greater than 2^{64}, then only the low-order 64 bits of the length are used. Thus the field contains the length of the original message, modulo 2^{64}.

The outcome of the first two steps yields a message that is an integer multiple of 512 bits in length. In Figure 12.6, the expanded message is represented as the sequence of 512-bit blocks Y_0, Y_1, . . ., Y_{L-1}, so that the total length of the expanded message is L × 512 bits. Equivalently, the result is a multiple of sixteen 32-bit words. Let M[0 . . . N-1] denote the words of the resulting message, with N an integer multiple of 16. Thus $N = L \times 16$.

- **Step 3: Initialize MD Buffer**

  A 128-bit buffer is used to hold intermediate and final results of the hash function. The buffer can be represented as four 32-bit registers (A, B, C, D). These registers are initialized to the following hexadecimal values (low-order octets first):

$$A = 01234567$$
$$B = 89ABCDEF$$
$$C = FEDCBA98$$
$$D = 76543210$$

- **Step 4: Process Message in 512-Bit (16-Word) Blocks**

  The heart of the algorithm is a module that consists of four "rounds" of processing (H_{MD5} in the Figure 12.6). The four rounds have similar structure but each uses a different primitive logical function. The function makes use of AND, OR, and XOR operations and addition modulo 2^{32}.

- **Step 5: Output**

  After all L 512-bit blocks have been processed, the output from the Lth stage is the 128-bit message digest.

MD5 is used in a number of applications, including PGP. It has been intensively analyzed and appears to be extremely secure.

TIP

This chapter has only skimmed the surface of the nature of these algorithms. For an in-depth look, see the author's *Network and Internetwork Security* (Prentice-Hall, Inc.,1995).

CHAPTER 13

Choosing Your Passphrase

If anyone ever manages to get hold of a copy of your secret key ring, then your secret key remains secure if, and only if, the thief doesn't know and cannot guess your passphrase.

If you are careful about how you use your passphrase, no one should ever learn it by looking over your shoulder or finding a scrap of paper in your files or in your garbage.

So, how hard is it to guess a passphrase, and what can you do about it?

13.1 HOW TO GUESS A PASSPHRASE

If someone gains access to your secret ring, it will contain a copy of your secret key encrypted with a passphrase. Here is a crude way to guess the passphrase:

1. The thief loads your secret ring onto a system running PGP.
2. The thief adds your public key (it's public and so obtainable) to the corresponding public key ring.
3. The thief tries to perform an operation requiring the secret key and enters a passphrase when PGP prompts for one.
4. If PGP continues the operation, the thief has guessed your passphrase.

This method is far too slow to be successful. Instead, the

process needs to be automated. Your secret key includes your public key as part of its data structure. Therefore, all the thief has to do is write a program that decrypts your secret key and compares the public key information that comes out with your actual public key. Then the thief writes another program that automatically tries a long list of potential passphrases until it finds the right one.

Such a program is called a password cracker. How fast can a cracker run through a list of potential passphrases? A comparable type of password cracker is one used to guess passwords on UNIX systems. UNIX uses a complicated form of the encryption algorithm DES, whereas PGP uses IDEA to encrypt passphrases. The UNIX DES should run slower than IDEA, so the performance of a UNIX password cracker gives us a conservative estimate.

As an example, the fastest password cracker known to the author was reported on the Internet in August 1993.[1] Using a Thinking Machines Corporation parallel computer, a performance of 1,560 encryptions per second per vector unit was achieved. With four vector units per processing node (a standard configuration), this works out to 800,000 encryptions per second on a 128-node machine (which is a modest size) and 6.4 million encryptions per second on a 1,024-node machine.

Even these stupendous guessing rates don't yet make it feasible for an attacker to use a dumb brute-force technique of trying all possible combinations of characters to discover a password. Instead, password crackers rely on the fact that some people choose easily guessable passwords. Unfortunately, human nature makes this line of attack practical. Some users, when permitted to choose their own password, pick one that is absurdly short. The results of one study at Purdue University are shown in Table 13.1. The study observed password change choices on 54 machines, representing approximately 7,000 user accounts. Almost 3% of the passwords were three characters or fewer in length! An attacker could begin the attack by exhaustively testing all possible passwords of length 3 or fewer.

Alas, password length is only part of the problem. Many people pick a password that is guessable, such as their wife's name, their street name, a dictionary word, and so forth. This makes the

---

[1] Madsen, J. "World Record in Password Checking." *Usenet, comp.security.misc newsgroup,* August 18,1993.

Table **13.1**

Observed Password Lengths

Length	Number	Fraction of Total
1	55	.004
2	87	.006
3	212	.02
4	449	.03
5	1260	.09
6	3035	.22
7	2917	.21
8	5772	.42
Total	13787	1.0

job of password cracking straightforward. The cracker simply has to test the password file against lists of likely passwords.

One demonstration of the effectiveness of guessing is reported by D. Klein.[2] From a variety of sources, the author collected UNIX password files containing nearly 14,000 encrypted passwords. The result, which the author rightly characterizes as frightening, is shown in Table 13.2. In all, nearly one-fourth of the passwords were guessed. Following is the strategy that was used:

1. Try the user's name, initials, account name, and other relevant personal information. In all, 130 different permutations for each user were tried.
2. Try words from various dictionaries. The author compiled a dictionary of over 60,000 words, including the on-line dictionary on the system itself, and various other lists as shown.
3. Try various permutations on the words from step 2. This included making the first letter uppercase or a control character, making the entire word uppercase, reversing the word, changing the letter "o" to the digit "zero," and so on. These permutations added another 1 million words to the list.

[2] Klein, D. "Foiling the Cracker: A Survey of, and Improvements to, Password Security." *Proceedings, UNIX Security Workshop II*, August 1990.

Table **13.2**

Passwords Cracked from a Sample Set of 13,797 Accounts

Type of Password	Search Size	Number of Matches	Percentage of Passwords Matched
User/account name	130	368	2.7%
Character sequences	866	22	0.2%
Numbers	427	9	0.1%
Chinese	392	56	0.4%
Place names	628	82	0.6%
Common names	2239	548	4.0%
Female names	4280	161	1.2%
Male names	2866	140	1.0%
Uncommon names	4955	130	0.9%
Myths & legends	1246	66	0.5%
Shakespearean	473	11	0.1%
Sports terms	238	32	0.2%
Science fiction	691	59	0.4%
Movies and actors	99	12	0.1%
Cartoons	92	9	0.1%
Famous people	290	55	0.4%
Phrases and patterns	933	253	1.8%
Surnames	33	9	0.1%
Biology	58	1	0.0%
System dictionary	19683	1027	7.4%
Machine names	9018	132	1.0%
Mnemonics	14	2	0.0%
King James bible	7525	83	0.6%
Miscellaneous words	3212	54	0.4%
Yiddish words	56	0	0.0%
Asteroids	2407	19	0.1%
TOTAL	62727	3340	24.2%

4. Try various capitalization permutations on the words from step 2 that weren't considered in step 3. This added almost 2 million additional words to the list.

Thus, the test involved in the neighborhood of 3 million words. Using the fastest Thinking Machines implementation listed earlier, the time to encrypt all these words is under one second. Yet in that half a second, the test has a 25% chance of guessing any particular password!

13.2 HOW TO CHOOSE AN UNGUESSABLE PASSPHRASE

The lesson from the two experiments just described (Tables 13.1 and 13.2) is that, left to their own devices, many users choose a password that is too short or too easy to guess. At the other extreme, if users are assigned passwords consisting of eight randomly selected printable characters, password cracking is effectively impossible.

Let's see how that works. Suppose we limit ourselves to the upper-case letters, the lower-case letters and the ten digits. That gives us an "alphabet" of 62 characters. The number of possible 8-character passwords from this alphabet is

$$8^{62} \approx 10^{55} \text{ passwords}$$

Suppose I am guessing 6.4 million (6.4 × 106) passwords per second. How long would it take to try all possible passwords of 8 characters? The answer is:

$$\frac{10^{55} \text{ passwords}}{6.4 \times 10^6 \text{ passwords / second}} = 1.53 \times 10^{49} \text{ seconds}$$

This works out to about 5×10^{41} years!

Unfortunately, it would be almost as difficult for most users to remember a password consisting of randomly chosen characters as it would be for someone else to guess it. Fortunately, even if we limit the password universe to strings of characters that are reasonably memorable, the size of the universe is still too large to permit practical cracking. Our goal, then, is to eliminate guessable passwords while allowing you to select a password that is memorable.

First, a couple of *don'ts*. Don't make the passphrase too long.

A long passphrase (say more than 10 characters) becomes tedious to type in, causing errors. Also, don't use too many oddball characters; these are unnatural to type and again lead to errors. With those restrictions, there are still plenty of possibilities.

A simple but effective strategy, recommended to its customers by the on-line service Compuserve, is to combine two unrelated words, separated by a non-alphanumeric character. A phrase such as kumquat/isobar is fairly easy to remember and type, but quite difficult to guess.

Table **13.3**

Strategies for User Selection of Easily Remembered Passwords

(a) Lines of a chosen childhood verse

Verse Line	Password
One for the money	14munny
Two for the show	24show
Three to get ready	32ready
Four to go (to)	42goto

(b) Expressions inspired by name of city

City	Intermediate Expression	Password
Paris	I love Paris in the springtime	ILPITST
Rome	Three (bright) coins in the (Trevi) fountain	TBCITTF
New York	The sidewalks of New York City	TSWONYC
San Francisco	I left my heart in San Francisco	ILMHISF

(c) Foods disliked during childhood

Food	Password
chocolate-covered peanuts	chocovpea
Pepsi-Cola (and) pretzels	pepcolpre
pineapple-cocoanut suckers	pincocsuc
fried (-) eggplant	frieggpla

(continued)

Table **13.3** *(continued)*

Strategies for User Selection of Easily Remembered Passwords
(d) Transform Techniques

Transform	Illustrative Expression	Password
Transliteration	Photographic	fotografik
	Schizophrenic	skitsofrenik
Interweaving of characters in successive words	duke, iron	diurkoen
	tent pole	tepontle
Translation	strangers	etraniere
Replacement of letter by decimal digit (mod 10 index of letter in natural order)	cabbage	3122175
Replacement of decimal number	10/12/1492	jabadib
Shift from "home" position on keyboard	zucchini	xivvjomo
Substitution of synonyms	coffee break	javarest
Substitution of antonyms	stoplight	startdark
Actuation of keyboard "shift"	6/6/1944	^?^?!($$
Substitution of abbreviations	relative humidity	relhum
Substitution of acronyms	Mothers Against Drunk Drivers, National Organization for Women	maddnow
Repetition	pan	panpan
Imagistic manipulation (180 degrees rotation of letters)	swimshow	smiwshom

One of the best sets of guidelines for choosing passwords came out of a study by A. Alvare.[3] Table 13.3 summarizes the suggestions. It should go without saying that you shouldn't use any of the particular passwords in this table. In fact, I would even recommend not using any of the specific strategies in Table 13.3, but rather treating this table as a source of inspiration. Good luck!

---

[3] Alvare, A. "How Crackers Crack Passwords or What Passwords to Avoid." *Proceedings, UNIX Security Workshop II*, August 1990.

Where to Get PGP

One of the best lists of locations for obtaining PGP is maintained by Michael Paul Johnson. The document, with the file name getpgp.asc, is maintained at two ftp sites on the Internet:

```
ftp.csn.net/mpj
ftp.netcom.com/pubmpj
```

The remainder of this chapter contains the version of this file available at the time this book went to press. I am grateful to Mike Johnson for permission to reproduce this material.

WHERE TO GET THE PRETTY GOOD PRIVACY PROGRAM (PGP)

(Last modified: 7 September 1994 by Mike Johnson)

WHAT IS THE LATEST VERSION?

There is more than one latest version. Pick one or more of the following that best suits your computer, patent restrictions, and export restrictions. Some countries (like France) may also restrict import or even use of strong cryptography like PGP.

Platform(s)	Latest Version	Distribution File Names
DOS, UNIX, or WinCIM/CSNav	Viacrypt PGP 2.7	disk sets
DOS, UNIX, others	MIT PGP 2.6.1	pgp261.zip (DOS +docs)
		pgp261s.zip (source)
		pg261s.zip (source on CompuServe)
		pgp261.tar.gz (source)
		pgp261.gz (same as above on DOS)
		pgp261.tar.Z (source)
		pgp261dc.zip (documentation)
		pgp261d.zip (docs on CompuServe)
Macintosh	MIT PGP 2.6	MacPGP2.6.sea.hqx (binary + docs)
		macpgp26.hqx (same as above)
		MacPGP2.6.src.sea.hqx (source)
		macpgp26.src (same as above)
		MacPGP2.6-68000.sea.hqx (binary)
		mcpgp268.hqx (same as above)
Mac Applescript	MacPGP 2.6ui v 1.2	MacPGP-2.6ui-v1.2.sit.hqx
		MacPGP-2.6ui_V1.2_sources.cpt.hqx
		MacPGP2.6uiV1.2en.cpt.hqx
		MacPGP2.6uiV1.2src.cpt.hqx
		MacPGP2.6uiV1.2.68000.hqx
Amiga	Amiga PGP 2.3a.4	PGPAmi23a_4.1ha
Atari	Atari PGP 2.6ui	pgp26uib.lzh (binary, docs)
		pgp26uis.lzh
Archimedes	Archimedes 2.3a	ArcPGP23a

Note: there are other versions available, but these are either old, or outside of the mainstream PGP project. Look for signatures from one of three sources: Viacrypt (Commercial), jis@mit.edu (North American freeware), or mathew@mantis.co.uk (the unofficial international version source). The "unofficial international" versions are really just PGP 2.3a, modified just enough to make it compatible with MIT PGP 2.6, but do not include all of the fixes in MIT PGP 2.6 and MIT PGP 2.6.1. They are named pgp26ui* or have a "ui" somewhere in their file names. I recommend the use of the "ui" versions only if:

(1) You are using a Macintosh;
(2) You are using a platform for which there is no Viacrypt or MIT PGP;
(3) You are outside of North America, and can't obtain Viacrypt or MIT PGP; or
(4) You need to use a key longer than 1024 bits (i. e. a 1264 bit key generated with PGP 2.3a or PGP 2.6ui).

WHERE CAN I GET VIACRYPT PGP?

If you are a commercial user of PGP in the USA or Canada, contact Viacrypt in Phoenix, Arizona, USA. The commecial version of PGP is fully licensed to use the patented RSA and IDEA encryption algorithms in commercial applications, and may be used in corporate environments in the USA and Canada. It is fully compatible with, functionally the same as, and just as strong as the freeware version of PGP. Due to limitations on ViaCrypt's RSA distribution license, ViaCrypt only distributes executable code and documentation for it, but they are working on making PGP available for a variety of platforms. Call or write to them for the latest information. The latest version number for their version of PGP is 2.7.

The Windows version is anticipated to ship by (or before) September 15, 1994; the Macintosh version is expected to ship in early October. The formal announcements will go out about one week prior to first ship dates. The Windows version is a high grade Visual Basic front end with the DOS program in the back end. It is a point-and-click, drag-and-drop operation.

Here is a brief summary of Viacrypt's currently-available products:

1. ViaCrypt PGP for MS-DOS. Prices start at $99.98
2. ViaCrypt PGP for UNIX. Includes executables for the following platforms:

> SunOS 4.1.x (SPARC)
> IBM RS/6000 AIX
> HP 9000 Series 700/800 UX

SCO 386/486 UNIX
SGI IRIX
AViiON DG-UX(88/OPEN)

Prices start at $149.98

Executables for the following additional platforms are available upon request for an additional $30.00 charge.

BSD 386
Ultrix MIPS DECstation 4.x

3. ViaCrypt PGP for WinCIM/CSNav. A special package for users of CompuServe. Prices start at $119.98

In September, 1994, ViaCrypt intends to announce two new major product additions:

ViaCrypt PGP for Windows
ViaCrypt PGP for Macintosh

Prices start at $124.98

Viacrypt's licensing and price information is as follows:

ViaCrypt PGP Version 2.7 for Windows	(Single User	$ 124.98
ViaCrypt PGP Version 2.7 for Windows	(Five User)	$ 374.98
ViaCrypt PGP Version 2.7 for Macintosh	(Single User)	$ 124.98
ViaCrypt PGP Version 2.7 for Macintosh	(Five User)	$ 374.98
ViaCrypt PGP Version 2.7 for MS-DOS	(Single User)	$ 99.98
ViaCrypt PGP Version 2.7 for MS-DOS	(Five User)	$ 299.98
ViaCrypt PGP Version 2.7 for UNIX	(Single User)	$ 149.98
ViaCrypt PGP Version 2.7 for UNIX	(Five User)	$ 449.98
ViaCrypt PGP for WinCIM/CSNav	(Single User)	$ 119.98
ViaCrypt PGP for WinCIM/CSNav	(Five User)	$ 359.98

UNIX platforms of Ultrix and BSD 386 have an additional $30.00 charge per platform.

Please contact ViaCrypt for pricing of 20 users and above.

Orders may be placed by calling 800-536-2664 during the hours of 8:30am to 5:00pm MST, Monday–Friday. We accept VISA, MasterCard, AMEX and Discover credit cards. If you have further questions, please feel free to contact:

Paul E. Uhlhorn
Director of Marketing, ViaCrypt Products
Mail: 9033 N. 24th Avenue, Suite 7
               Phoenix AZ 85021-2847
Phone: (602) 944-0773
Fax: (602) 943-2601
Internet: viacrypt@acm.org
Compuserve: 70304.41

WHERE CAN I GET THE FREEWARE PGP?

These listings are subject to change without notice. If you find that PGP has been removed from any of these sites, please let me know so that I can update this list. Likewise, if you find PGP on a good site elsewhere (especially on any BBS that allows first time callers to access PGP for free), please let me know so that I can update this list. Because this list changes frequently, I have not attempted to keep it complete, but there should be enough pointers to let you easily find PGP.

There are several ways to get the freeware PGP: ftp, WWW, BBS, CompuServe, America Online (maybe), email ftp server, and sneakernet (ask a friend for a copy). Just don't ask the author directly for a copy.

FTP SITES IN NORTH AMERICA

These sites generally have some mechanism to (1) discourage export of PGP and violation of the ITAR, (2) protect the site operators from harrassment by the Federal Government, and (3) still

allow automated distribution of PGP as far as is allowed under all
applicable laws.

Telnet to net-dist.mit.edu, log in as getpgp, answer the questions, then ftp to net-dist.mit.edu and change to the hidden directory named in the telnet session to get your own copy.

MIT-PGP is for U. S. and Canadian use only, but MIT is only distributing it within the USA (due to some archaic export control laws).

1. Read `ftp://net-dist.mit.edu/pub/` `PGP/mitlicen. txt` and agree to it.
2. Read `ftp://net-dist.mit.edu/pub/PGP/rsalicen.txt` and agree to it.
3. Telnet to `net-dist.mit.edu` and log in as `getpgp`.
4. Answer the questions and write down the directory name listed.
5. QUICKLY end the telnet session with ^C and ftp to the indicated directory on `net-dist.mit.edu` (something like `/pub/PGP/dist/U.S.-only-????`) and get the distribution files (see the above chart for names).

If the hidden directory name is invalid, start over at step 3, above.

You can also get PGP from:

`ftp.csn.net/mpj`
   `ftp://ftp.csn.net/mpj/I_will_not_export/crypto_???????/pgp/`
   See `ftp://ftp.csn.net/mpj/README.MPJ` for the ???????
   See `ftp://ftp.csn.net/mpj/help` for more help on negotiating this site's export control methods (open to USA and Canada).

`ftp.netcom.com/pub/mpj`
   `ftp://ftp.netcom.com/mpj/I_will_not_export`
          `/crypto_???????/pgp/`
   See `ftp://ftp.netcom.com/pub/mpj/README.MPJ` for the ???????
   See `ftp://ftp.netcom.com/pub/mpj/help` for more help on negotiating this site's export control methods.

TO GET THESE FILES BY EMAIL, send mail to
ftp-request@netcom.com containing the word HELP in
the body of the message for instructions. You will have to
work quickly to get README.MPJ then the files before the
??????? part of the path name changes again (several
times a day).

ftp.eff.org
Follow the instructions found in README.Dist that you get
from one of:

ftp://ftp.eff.org/pub/Net_info/Tools/Crypto/README.Dist
gopher.eff.org, 1/Net_info/Tools/Crypto
gopher://gopher.eff.org/11/Net_info/Tools/Crypto
http://www.eff.org/pub/Net_info/Tools/Crypto/

ftp.wimsey.bc.ca
/pub/crypto/software/dist/US_or_Canada_only_XXXXXXX/PGP
(U. S. and Canadian users only)
See /pub/crypto/software/README for the characters
for XXXXXXXX
This site has all public releases of the freeware PGP.

WORLD WIDE WEB ACCESS

http://www.matnis.co.uk/pgp/pgp.html
http://rschp2.anu.edu.au:8080/crypt.html

COMPUSERVE

The NCSA Forum sysops have a library (Library 12: Export
Controlled) that is available only to people who send them a message asserting that they are within the U.S.A. This library contains PGP. I have also seen PGP in some other places on
Compuserve. Try searching for PGP261.ZIP in the IBMFF forum
for up-to-date information on PGP in selected other areas. The last
time I tried a search like this, PGP 2.6 was found in the PC World
Online forum (GO PWOFORUM) new uploads area, along with several PGP shells and accessories. I've also heard that EUROFORUM
caries PGP 2.6ui, but have not confirmed this.

   Compuserve file names are even more limited than DOS (6.3
instead of the already lame 8.3), so the file names to look for are

`PGP26.ZIP`, `PGP261S.ZIP` (source code), `PGP261.GZ` (Unix source code) and `PGP261D.ZIP` (documentation only).

BULLETIN BOARD SYSTEMS

Colorado Catacombs BBS
>   Mike Johnson, sysop
>   Mac and DOS versions of PGP, PGP shells, and some other crypto stuff.
>   Also the home of some good Bible search files and some shareware written by Mike Johnson, including DLOCK, CRYPTA, CRYPTE, CRYPTMPJ, MCP, MDIR, DELETE, PROVERB, SPLIT, ONEPAD, etc.
>   v.FAST/v.32bis/v.42bis, speeds up to 28,800 bps
>   8 data bits, 1 stop, no parity, as fast as your modem will go.
>   Use ANSI terminal emulation, of if you can't, try VT-100.
>   Free access to PGP. If busy or no answer, try again later.
>   Log in with your own name, or if someone else has already used that, try a variation on your name or pseudonym. You can request access to crypto software on line, and if you qualify legally under the ITAR, you can download on the first call.
>   For free access: log in with your own name, answer the questions, then select [Q]uestionaire 3 from the [M]ain menu.
>   (303) 772-1062 Longmont, Colorado number — 2 lines.
>   (303) 938-9654 Boulder, Colorado number forwarded to Longmont number intended for use by people in the Denver, Colorado area.

Hieroglyphics Voodoo Machine (Colorado)
>   Jim Still (aka Johannes Keppler), sysop.
>   DOS, OS2, and Mac versions.
>   (303) 443-2457
>   For free access for PGP, DLOCK, Secure Drive, etc., log in as "VOO DOO" with the password "NEW" (good for 30 minutes access to free files).

Exec-Net (New York)
>   Host BBS for the ILink net.
>   (914) 667-4567

The Ferret BBS (North Little Rock, Arkansas)
   (501) 791-0124 also (501) 791-0125
   Special PGP users account:
   login name: PGP USER
   password: PGP
   This information from: Jim Wenzel
           <jim.wenzel@grapevine.lrk.ar.us>

Other BBS — check your local BBS. Chances are good that it has any release that is at least a month old if it has much of a file area at all.

AMERICA ONLINE:

Try PC WORLD soft/lib. (key word PGP). Make sure you get ALL of the files, including the documentation. Somebody apparently split up the .ZIP file just to make life more difficult.

OTHER FTP SITES

These other ftp sites don't have the "export control" hoops to jump through that most North American sites have in deference to archaic laws.

        ftp.informatik.uni-hamburg.de
        /pub/virus/crypt/pgp
This site has most, if not all, of the current PGP files.

        black.ox.ac.uk   (129.67.1.165)

ftp.netcom.com
/pub/dcosenza -- Some crypto stuff, sometimes includes PGP.
/pub/gbe/pgpfaq.asc – Frequently asked questions
   answered.
/pub/qwerty – How to MacPGP Guide, largest steganography ftp site as well. PGP FAQ, crypto FAQ, US Crypto
   Policy FAQ, Steganograpy software list. MacUtilites for
   use with MacPGP. Stealth1.1 + other steganography
   programs. Send mail to qwerty@netcom.com with the
   subject "Bomb me!" to get the PGP FAQ and MacPGP
   guide if you don't have ftp access.

```
ftp.ee.und.ac.za
 /pub/crypto/pgp
```

```
soda.berkeley.edu
 /pub/cypherpunks/pgp
```
 (DOS, Mac)

```
ftp.demon.co.uk
 /pub/amiga/pgp
 /pub/archimedes
 /pub/pgp
 /pub/mac/MacPGP
```

```
ftp.informatik.tu-muenchen.de
```

```
ftp.funet.fi
```

```
ftp.dsi.unimi.it
/pub/security/crypt/PGP
```

```
ftp.tu-clausthal.de (139.174.2.10)
```
  (Atari ST/E,TT,Falcon)
```
 /pub/atari/misc/pgp/pgp26uib.lzh
```
  (2.6ui ttp, 2.3a docs)
```
 /pub/atari/misc/pgp/pgp26uis.lzh
```
  (2.6ui sources)
```
 /pub/atari/misc/pgp/pgp26ui.diffs
```
  (Atari diffs for 2.6 sources)

```
wuarchive.wustl.edu
 /pub/aminet/util/crypt
```

```
src.doc.ic.ac.uk
```
 (Amiga)
```
 /aminet
 /amiga-boing
```

```
ftp.informatik.tu-muenchen.de
 /pub/comp/os/os2/crypt/pgp23os2A.zip (OS/2)
```

```
iswuarchive.wustl.edu
 pub/aminet/util/crypt
```
 (Amiga)

```
nic.funet.fi   (128.214.6.100)
 /pub/crypt

ftp.uni-kl.de (131.246.9.95)
 /pub/aminet/util/crypt

qiclab.scn.rain.com (147.28.0.97)

pc.usl.edu (130.70.40.3)

leif.thep.lu.se (130.235.92.55)

goya.dit.upm.es (138.4.2.2)

tupac-amaru.informatik.rwth-aachen.de (137.226.112.31)

ftp.etsu.edu (192.43.199.20)

princeton.edu (128.112.228.1)

pencil.cs.missouri.edu (128.206.100.207)

soda.csua.berkeley.edu
 /PC/wuarchive/pgp/
```

Also, try an archie search for PGP using the command:

archie -s pgp2.6 (**DOS & Unix Versions**)
  archie -s pgp2.6 (**MAC Versions**)

FTPMAIL

For those individuals who do not have access to FTP, but do have access to e-mail, you can get FTP files mailed to you. For information on this service, send a message saying "Help" to ftpmail@decwrl.dec.com. You will be sent an instruction sheet on how to use the ftpmail service.

Another e-mail service is from nic.funet.fi. Send the following mail message to mailserv@nic.funet.fi:

```
ENCODER uuencode
SEND pub/crypt/pgp23srcA.zip
SEND pub/crypt/pgp23A.zip
```

This will deposit the two zipfiles, as 15 batched messages, in your mailbox with about 24 hours. Save and undecode.

For the ftp sites on netcom, send mail to: ftprequest@netcom.com containing the word HELP in the body of the message.

IS MY COPY OF PGP GOOD?

If you find a version of the PGP package that does not include the PGP User's Guide, something is wrong. The manual should always be included in the package. PGP should be signed by one of the developers (Philip Zimmermann, Jeff Schiller, Viacrypt, etc.). If it isn't, the package is suspect and should not be used or distributed. The site you found it on should remove it so that it does no further harm to others. To be really sure, you should get PGP directly from MIT or check the signatures with a version of PGP that you trust. The copies of PGP on ftp.csn.net/mpj, ftp.netcom.com/pub/mpj, and the Colorado Catacombs BBS are direct copies of the ones on MIT, except that the ones on the BBS include a BBS advertisement (automatically added by the system when it virus scans new files) in the outer .zip files.

OTHER PGP DOCUMENTATION

PGP is rather counter-intuitive to a Mac user. Luckily, there's a guide to using MacPGP in ftp://ftp.netcom.com/pub/qwerty/Here.is.How.to.MacPGP.

There is a Frequently Asked Questions document in ftp://ftp.netcom.com/pub/gbe/pgpfaq.asc

For more information on the "time bomb" in PGP, see ftp://ftp/netcom.com/pub/mpj/pgpbomb.asc

LANGUAGE MODULES

These are suitable for most PGP versions. I am not aware of any export/import restrictions on these files.

German

* _UK:_ ftp://black.ox.ac.uk/src/security/pgp_german.txt
* _US:_ ftp://ftp.csn.net/mpj/public/pgp/pgp_german.txt
* _US:_ ftp://ftp.csn.net/mpj/public/pgp/PGP_german_docs.lha

Italian

* _IT:_
ftp://ftp.dsi.unimi.it/pub/security/crypt/PGP/pgp-lang.italian.tar.gz
* _FI:_
ftp://ftp.funet.fi/pub/crypt/ghost.dsi.unimi.it/PGP/pgplang.italian.tar.gz
* _US:_ ftp://ftp.csn.net/mpj/public/pgp/pgp-lang.italian.tar.gz

Japanese

* _US:_ ftp://ftp.csn.net/mpj/public/pgp/pgp-msgs-japanese.tar.gz

Lithuanian

* _US:_ ftp://ftp.csn.net/mpj/public/pgp/pgp231tk.zip

Russian

* _RU:_ ftp://ftp.kiae.su/unix/crypto/pgp/pgp26ru.zip
                    (MIT version)
* _RU:_ ftp://ftp.kiae.su/unix/crypto/pgp/pgp26uir.zip
                    (ui version)
* _US:_ ftp://ftp.csn.net/mpj/public/pgp/pgp26ru.zip

Spanish

* _IT:_
ftp://ftp.dsi.unimi.it/pub/security/crypt/PGP/pgp-lang.spanish.tar.gz
* _FI:_
ftp://ftp.funet.fi/pub/crypt/ghost.dsi.unimi.it/pgp-lang.spanish.tar.gz
* _US:_ ftp://ftp.csn.net/mpj/public/pgp/pgp-lang.spanish.tar.gz

Swedish

* _UK:_ ftp://black.ox.ac.uk/src/security/pgp_swedish.txt
* _US:_ ftp://ftp.csn.net/mpj/public/pgp/pgp_swedish.txt

ARCHIE WHO?

There are many more sites. You can use archie and/or other "net-surfing" tools to find a more up-to-date listing, if desired.

WHAT IS ALL THIS NONSENSE ABOUT EXPORT CONTROLS?

For a detailed rant, get `ftp://ftp.csn.net/mpj/cryptusa.zip`

The practical meaning, until the law is corrected to make sense, is that you are requested to get PGP from sites outside of the USA and Canada if you are outside of the USA and Canada. If you are in France, I understand that you aren't even supposed import it. Other countries may be worse.

It is illegal to export PGP from the USA to any country except Canada, even if that version of PGP originated outside of the USA. Don't do it. Don't ask me to do it. The law is not rational, but it exists, and the Federal Government has no sense of humor. On the other hand, if you should discover a copy of PGP in some place other than the USA, then you are bound by the laws of both that country and your own country with respect to what you can do with it, not necessarily by U. S. Law. Your laws may be more or less restrictive, and may possibly refer to U. S. Law through some sort of treaty. If you live in a place where you can freely distribute and use PGP, then I applaud your government.

In spite of the best efforts of MIT and the other primary developers and distributors of PGP not to violate the International Traffic in Arms Regulations, MIT PGP has been observed to migrate to many foreign sites. Whoever is responsible for this export is responsible for their own actions and is not encouraged or endorsed by myself, Philip Zimmermann, or MIT. This doesn't necessarily mean that we agree with the law, or even that the law itself is Constitutional. It just means that becoming a test case is not fun.

WHAT INTELLECTUAL PROPERTY RESTRICTIONS EXIST IN THE USA?

MIT PGP is only for noncommercial use because of restrictions on the licensing of both the RSA algorithm (attached to RSAREF) and the IDEA algorithm. PKP/RSADSI insist that we use RSAREF instead of the mpi library for reasons that make sense to them.

For commercial use, use Viacrypt PGP, which is fully licensed to use both the RSA and IDEA algorithms in commercial and corporate environments.

WHAT INTELLECTUAL PROPERTY RESTRICTIONS EXIST IN CANADA?

MIT PGP is only for noncommercial use because of restrictions on the licensing of the IDEA algorithm. Because the RSA algorithm isn't patented in Canada, you are free to use the mpi library instead of RSAREF, if you want to, thus freeing yourself of the RSAREF license.

For commercial use, use Viacrypt PGP, which is fully licensed to use the IDEA algorithm in commercial and corporate environments.

WHAT INTELLECTUAL PROPERTY RESTRICTIONS EXIST OUTSIDE NORTH AMERICA?

MIT PGP is only for noncommercial in areas where there is a patent on software implementations of the IDEA algorithm. Because the RSA algorithm isn't patented outside of the USA, you are free to use the mpi library instead of RSAREF, if you want to, thus freeing yourself of the RSAREF license.

For commercial use, you cannot buy Viacrypt PGP, but you can arrange to license your use of IDEA directly from ETH Zurich. If software implementations of IDEA are not covered by a patent in your country, then you can use the freeware versions of PGP, provided that you compile it with the mpi library instead of RSAREF.

WHAT IS THE "TIME BOMB" IN MIT PGP 2.6?

As a concession to the RSA patent holders (in return for endorsement of the legality of the freeware MIT PGP 2.6), MIT placed an inducement in MIT PGP 2.6 to encourage upgrade from the allegedly patent-infringing PGP 2.3a to the MIT version. The nature of this inducement is a change in a packet ID byte that causes PGP 2.3a and earlier to reject messages created by MIT PGP 2.6 after 1 September 1994. Altering MIT PGP 2.6 to bypass this annoyance (though technically an easy change to the LEGAL_KLUDGE), invalidates the blessing of Public Key Partners on the licence of MIT PGP 2.6. Therefore, it is a bad idea. On the other hand, it is trivial to hack PGP 2.3a to accept these packets, and that (plus a few other bug fixes) is essentially what PGP 2.6ui is. None of the versions of PGP greater than 2.3 have problems reading the old packet ID values, so for maximum compatibility, the ideal is to write the old value and accept either value.

Unfortunately, this time bomb has a negative effect on Viacrypt PGP 2.4, as well, which never infringed on anyone's patents. Viacrypt's solution was to issue PGP 2.7, which, by default acts just like MIT PGP 2.6, but has a config.txt option (explained in the release) that allows compatibility with both PGP 2.4 and PGP 2.6. Naturally, this also allows compatibility with PGP 2.3a.

The time bomb is annoying for those who still wish to use PGP 2.3a, and for those who use Viacrypt PGP 2.4 and don't want to spend US$10 to upgrade to Viacrypt PGP 2.7, but considering the magnitude of the concession made by Public Key Partners in legitimizing the freeware PGP for use in the USA, it was worth it.

For more information on the time bomb, see
ftp://ftp.csn.net/mpj/pgpbomb.asc

ARE MY KEYS COMPATIBLE WITH THE OTHER PGP VERSIONS?

If your RSA key modulus length is less than or equal to 1024 bits (I don't recommend less, unless you have a really slow computer and little patience), and if your key was generated in the PKCS format, then it will work with any of the current PGP versions (MIT PGP 2.6, PGP 2.6ui, or Viacrypt PGP 2.7). If this is not the case, you really should generate a new key that qualifies.

Philip Zimmermann is aware of the desire for longer keys in PGP by some PGP fans (like me), but wants to migrate towards that goal in an orderly way, by first releasing versions of PGP for all platforms and for both commercial (Viacrypt) and freeware (MIT) flavors that ACCEPT long keys, then releasing versions that can also GENERATE long keys. He also has some other neat key management ideas that he plans to implement in future versions.

BUGS

These are the most annoying:

MIT PGP 2.6 — the function `xorbytes` doesn't. Replace the = with ^= to fix it. The effect of this bug is that RSA keys aren't quite as random as they should be -- probably not a practical problem, but worth fixing if you are going to compile the code yourself. Fixed in 2.6.1.

MIT PGP 2.6 — DON'T SET `PGPPASS` when editing your keys, because if you do, and if you don't change your pass phrase, the key is lost. (If this happens, rename your backup keyring files to the primary files before you do anything else). Fixed in 2.6.1.

PGP 2.6ui — Conventional encryption -c option doesn't use a different IV every time, like it is supposed to. (PGP 2.3a had this problem, too). Fixed in 2.6 and 2.6.1.

Public Key Servers

Public key servers are facilities maintained by public-spirited PGP users for the benefit of the entire PGP community. Anyone can post his or her public key on the server, and anyone can access a server to get a copy of someone's public key. Most of these servers are interlocked: If you send your key to one server, it is automatically passed on to the other servers. This saves you the trouble of multiple postings and saves others the trouble of multiple searches.

The principal deficiency with a public key server is that it doesn't guarantee integrity. No attempt is made to verify the identity of anyone posting to the server. Therefore, if you do post to a server, your key should come equipped with certifying signatures, so that others may trust the key. If you obtain a key from a server, you shouldn't trust its validity unless it is signed by someone you trust or unless you take further steps to verify its validity.

This chapter begins with a concise user's guide to public key servers. Next, we list some locations of public key servers. Finally, we introduce a service that is similar to a public key server, but that provides additional services for a fee.

15.1 HOW TO USE PUBLIC KEY SERVERS

Finger Access

The most convenient means of access to a public key server is with the finger command, described in Section 6.1. At least one server, the one at wasabi.io.com, provides a finger interface. If you are on the Internet, you can get current information about this server by typing the command:

        finger @wasabi.io.com

After a short pause, the following response should appear on your screen:

```
[wasabi.io.com]
This is the PGP Key finger server at wasabi.io.com.

To find a key, first search by name, for example:

        finger prz@wasabi.io.com

Note you can search for strings which contain user@host...

        finger explorer@iastate@wasabi.io.com

Once you have found the key ID after asking by name, do:

        finger 0xF605A5@wasabi.io.com

Note that the 0x is important when asking for a key by ID.
```

For example, suppose you want to get Phil Zimmermann's key and you know that his e-mail address begins with prz. Enter the command

        finger prz@wasabi.io.com

Back comes:

```
[wasabi.io.com]
pub   1024/C7A966DD 1993/05/21 Philip R. Zimmermann
<prz@acm.org>

pub    512/23C4949D 1994/02/23 Ole Hesprzich
<o.hesprzich@a-link-h.han.de>

pub    384/34826919 1994/01/19 Ole Hesprzich
<o.hesprzich@a-link-h.han.de>
```

There are three items that match "prz" somewhere in their User ID. The first entry is the one you want. Note the Key ID and then enter:

        finger 0xC7A966DD@wasabi.io.com

Back comes:

```
[wasabi.io.com]
-----BEGIN PGP PUBLIC KEY BLOCK-----
Version: 2.5

mQCNAiv8ZoAAAAEEAKc4d45hN5qFM79nWGLkrGWputWmtdxJk0BZEbi0kNRbJBC2
p10ASImd//cCDwLR2alBUSt8O2WGik9PBZgthjMOenoDmzKiG8BkE9AFKonyxvD2
lDnqbydXi+YQmOTsWSw4jTTSb3cflhVkf8hVUVpMFQThafV0CmV5hLjHqWbdAAUR
tCJQaGlsaXAgUi4gWmltbWVybWFubiA8cHJ6QGFjbS5vcmc+iQBVAgUQLeTVN1UF
ZvpNDE7hAQEspgH+L0jcCteJhBW3NwJaXygzDP4Lq/JNk2X7Pgy5wGPst1BZ58EM
km+mgP5PZTG/px3DyFsMcuBQP+xZfrxWge1714kAlQIFEC3LGYtleYS4x6lm3QEB
uTMD/iaTje7mA8B2hVs8PDM1Z2nhOd2oMHwGJI4fy8H7SQSVPHV3BlRZpkIou0/v
bEZY9b8WlUm9QEETWZEMmKYgHZTbEzkkFtq0zNqgfsuORoe262c/pbYofNrMmnYo
k7K3vIAoqbUV6J1RRJ0oo3y+8IMifjnNZKfgNpGmJDCMTh8MiQCVAgUQLPurleYM
uhadwVTRAQH09AQAqCIpsH7zVMdLhQs8/VgiRferWWjujiAbQFViTee2BM0sa4wc
uNjO42pBR7CILT5HXbmHxjQof9cIQO76sSUyKEkVXPuY+TaBNcdnbZvj9jsDuQAn
Dvl1IL9j5YIBbQEPYqeUGb1td7GEwt1ULTbKwhaTV2LaqrzKuU3a9QVLmtuJAJUC
BRAsHjxc9MoAgY3nItkBAda3A/9EGIs83h2e3yyb2pm0rQc9hXSF91ngiJJ9HRXn
a4ooxCwisEnHZzlna+6sEt4qSHw55x/9f5mHaYR6evKZH+6sEJ/zEZCfJM97Di3/
chDkpeyqLZu45PKyT0+ST5yrFlMRclBaLEHd9UqsKRHTbFtZxFdD+k+zQ5s4ThUu
1BPUbYkYAAIFECwdS9rKPaH9hlqn8wEBxFECWIVTcSAVB04aQLacK6kECK2b9HoK
Qq1rJNkdCt17kj+kJjRsZRzpqUSdK6plTID0cLV8yDSKqyozi+tDo9mvapXQhcNj
iaLJg1EnIokAlQIFECv8Z0bidd4O/2f3CwEBiv8EAKHivcNmyr0g7LaZx37QPSop
XRiZvzzsvDQqMgEouZQipdTDZZFufxsCev4YXSoYTrWgAd1JI3uktE6Z+OXucxVo4
Ncc7Fi4scCcdnRn8BCwtzlTTnk+bqtDmUqtJovjP2YQo1NYz2FANgxmkfigALyEj
P5qlgf7+EGN1H3DsAqW7
=SiOA
-----END PGP PUBLIC KEY BLOCK-----

Type bits/keyID    Date       User ID

pub  1024/C7A966DD 1993/05/21 Philip R. Zimmermann <prz@acm.org>

1 key(s) examined.
```

E-mail Access

The more common way to use a key server is by exchanging mail messages. First, you need the e-mail address of a server. For example, pgp-public-keys@pgp.ai.mit.edu is the address of a server maintained at MIT. All commands to the server are issued by sending a message with the command in the subject line. It is a good idea, the first time you use a server, to send the help command

Suppose that Bob sends the following e-mail message:

```
To: pgp-public-keys@pgp.ai.mit.edu
From: BobP@university.edu
Subject: help
```

The body of the message will be ignored and so should be empty. Bob will get back a reply message whose body is shown in Figure 15.1. As you can see there are only a few, simple commands.

Retrieving Keys　If you know the full User ID you are interested in, you can issue a GET command and the key server will return that one key, in ASCII armor. If you aren't sure of the whole User ID, but know part of it, issue an MGET command and the server will return all keys that match that partial User ID.

You can get the entire public key ring by simply issuing a blank GET command, with no information after the GET, and you can use the LAST command to get the most recent additions to the server.

A word of warning: public key servers contain thousands of keys. It can take literally hours to process all of these keys on your system, as PGP cross-checks signatures and trust levels. Unless you have some serious need for all those keys, it isn't worth issuing a blanket GET command. If you do want the entire key ring, a better way to get it is by ftp (file transfer protocol). Some key servers provide this capability.

Retrieving an Index　To help you determine whether a key of interest is on the public key server, issue the INDEX command. The server will send you back a listing similar to the public key display shown in Figure 5.2. The index shows, for each key, the key size, Key ID, Date, and User ID. The VERBOSE INDEX command retrieves a list of keys and their signatures, similar to the public key display shown in Figure 6.7.

Adding and Removing Your Key　You may add your key to a server by sending the server a message with the command ADD in the subject line and with the ASCII-armor version of your public key in the body of the text. Make sure the key is signed at least with your own signature.

If you add a User ID, simply send your key to the server

This keyserver is here to help transfer public keys between users. It does NOT attempt to guarantee that a particular public key is a valid key; use the signators on the key for that kind of security. This service can be discontinued at any time without prior notification.

This keyserver processes requests in the form of mail messages. The commands for the server are entered on the Subject: line.

```
To: pgp-public-keys@pgp.ai.mit.edu
From: johndoe@some.site.edu
Subject: help
```

For example, to add your key to this keyserver, or to update your key if it is already there, send a message similar to the following to this keyserver:

```
To: pgp-public-keys@pgp.ai.mit.edu
From: johndoe@some.site.edu
Subject: add

-----BEGIN PGP PUBLIC KEY BLOCK-----

<blah blah blah>

-----END PGP PUBLIC KEY BLOCK-----
```

COMPROMISED KEYS: Create a Key Revocation Certificate (read the PGP docs on how to do that) and mail your key to the server once again, with the ADD command.

Valid commands are:

Command	Message body contains
ADD	Your PGP public key (key to add is body of msg)
INDEX	List all PGP keys the server knows about (-kv)
VERBOSE INDEX	List all PGP keys, verbose format (-kvv)
GET	Get the whole public key ring (split)
GET userid	Get just that one key
MGET regexp	Get all keys which match /regexp/
LAST days	Get the keys updated in the last 'days' days

(continued)

Fig **15.1**   Information Supplied by a Key Server

Examples for the MGET command:

```
MGET michael    Gets all keys which have "michael" in them
MGET iastate    All keys which contain "iastate"
MGET F605A5|3A738B   Those two keyid's
```
Just try not to use ``MGET .*'' -- use "GET" instead.

Questions concerning this keyserver should be addressed to:

```
pgp-public-keys-request@pgp.ai.mit.edu
```

Requests to automatically synchronize this keyserver with other
keyservers should be sent to the above address

Fig **15.1**   Information Supplied by a Key Server   *(continued)*

again using an ADD command, and the server will add the new
information to your key.

There is no way to remove your key from the server; the only
thing you can do is send a revocation certificate, which the server
will attach to your key.

If you send your key to a server and get back a message of the
form "No new keys or signatures in keyfile," this means the key
that you sent, including all of its signatures, is already on the server. Either you already submitted the key and forgot or someone
else posted your key. To make sure, try GETing your key from the
server.

Advanced Key Searching — Regular Expressions

The MGET command uses what are known as regular expressions. A regular expression defines a set of one or more strings of
characters. A number of UNIX utilities use regular expressions to
search for and replace strings. This subsection provides an elementary introduction and is sufficient to give you quite a bit of flexibility in using MGET.

Consider the following regular expression:

```
company\.com
```

The following are examples of strings that satisfy this regular
expression:

```
Robert Person <RPerson@company.com>
Alpha Beta Corp <ABC@division.company.com>
user%division.company.com@elsewhere.net
```

Any string of characters that includes the sequence "company.com" satisfies the regular expression. In the regular expression, the period is immediately preceded by a backslash. The reason for this is that the period is one of the special characters that have a particular meaning in regular expressions. If you want to use a period as just a period and not a special character, you must precede it with the backslash. This is also true for other special characters: the backslash means that the next character is to be taken literally.

When used as a special character, the period acts as a wild-card and stands for any single character other than a character designating a new line (such as a carriage return or line feed). Another special character is the asterisk (*), which means "zero or more of the preceding character." So, if we have the regular expression

```
Person@.*\.com
```

each of the following is a match:

```
Robert Person <RPerson@company.com>
George Person <GPerson@store.com>
Person@service.com
```

But these are not matches:

```
Person@university.edu
Smith@company.com
```

In other words, strings that match this regular expression include the sequence of characters Person@ followed by zero or more arbitrary characters followed by .com.

Another important special character is the caret (^). If this appears at the beginning of a regular expression, it means that any matching string must start with the following sequence. So if we have the regular expression:

```
^Robert Person
```

Then this is a match:

```
Robert Person <RPerson@company.com>
```

but this is not

```
G. Robert Person <RPerson@company.com>
```

Another special character is the dollar sign ($). If this appears at the end of a regular expression, it means that any matching string must end with the following sequence. So if we have the regular expression:

```
@university.edu>$
```

Then, the following are matches:

```
Bob Person <BobP@university.edu>
Yulanda Strobe <YS@university.edu>
```

but this are not:

```
Yulanda Strobe <YS@university.edu> OR
        <yulanda@nonprofit.org>
```

The final special character we will discuss is the vertical bar (|). If two regular expressions are separated by a bar, then a string matching either expression is a match. For example, for the regular expression:

```
BobP | RPerson
```

both of the following are matches:

```
Bob Person <BobP@university.edu>
Robert Person <RPerson@company.com>
```

To summarize, here are the special characters we have reviewed:

Special Character	Interpretation
.	Any single character except newline
*	Zero or more of the single preceding character
^	A regular expression that begins with ^ can match a string only at the beginning of a line
$	A regular expression that ends with $ can match a string only at the end of a line
\	Interpret the single following character as itself and not as a special character
|	Two regular expressions separated by a | match an occurrence of either.

There is much more to the study of regular expressions, but this above summary will enable you to retrieve keys efficiently from a public server.

15.2 WHERE TO FIND PUBLIC KEY SERVERS

One of the best lists of locations of PGP public key servers is maintained by Gary Edstrom as part of the PGP FAQ (frequently asked questions). The FAQ consists of five files with the names pgpfaq01.asc, pgpfaq02.asc, pgpfaq03.asc, pgpfaq04.asc, and pgpfaq05.asc. These files are available via ftp at ftp.netcom.com:/pub/gbe and a number of other locations. The remainder of this section contains the list in the FAQ available at the time this book went to press. I am grateful to Gary Edstrom for permission to reproduce this material.

The following is a list of all of the known public key servers active as of the publication date of this FAQ. I try to keep this list current by requesting keys from a different server every few days on a rotating basis. Any changes to this list should be posted to alt.security.pgp and a copy forwarded to me for inclusion in future releases of the alt.security.pgp FAQ.

Internet sites:

```
pgp-public-keys@demon.co.uk
Mark Turner <mark@demon.co.uk>
FTP: ftp.demon.co.uk:/pub/pgp/pubring.pgp
Verified: 10-Apr-94
```

pgp-public-keys@fbihh.informatik.uni-hamburg.de
Vesselin V. Bontchev <bontchev@fbihh.informatik.uni-hamburg.de>
FTP:ftp.informatik.uni-hamburg.de:/pub/virus/misc/pubkring.pgp
Verified: 10-Apr-94

public-key-server@martigny.ai.mit.edu
Brian A. LaMacchia public-key-server-
request@martigny.ai.mit.edu>
FTP: None
Verified: 10-Apr-94

pgp-public-keys@pgp.ox.ac.uk
Paul Leyland <pcl@ox.ac.uk>
FTP: None
Verified: 11-Apr-94

pgp-public-keys@dsi.unimi.it
David Vincenzetti <vince@dsi.unimi.it>
FTP: ghost.dsi.unimi.it:/pub/crypt/public-keys.pgp
Verified: 10-Apr-94

pgp-public-keys@kub.nl
Teun Nijssen <teun@kub.nl>
FTP: None
Verified: 10-Apr-94

pgp-public-keys@ext221.sra.co.jp
Hironobu Suzuki <hironobu@sra.co.jp>
FTP: None
Verified: 11-Apr-94

pgp-public-keys@sw.oz.au
Jeremy Fitzhardinge <jeremy@sw.oz.au>
FTP: None
Verified: 8-Mar-94

pgp-public-keys@io.com
Sysop: pgpkeys@wasabi.io.com
FTP: wasabi.io.com:/pub/pgpkeys
        NNNNNN.asc for individual keys
        KV   pgp -kv listing
        KVV   pgp -kvv listing
        KXA.asc   full keyring (pgp -kxa listing)
        pgpkeys.tar.Z   all the above (for other archive sites)
        (This site does *not* hold a binary keyring)
Verified: 10-Apr-94

```
Server does not support "Last <n>" command
finger <userid>@wasabi.io.com — Returns all names matching
<userid>
finger <keyid>@wasabi.io.com - Returns armored key matching
<keyid>
finger         @wasabi.io.com - Returns help for finger server
Note: site name may change at some time in the future:
if wasabi.io.com doesn't exist, try pgp.io.com ...

pgp-public-keys@kiae.su
<blaster@rd.relcom.msk.su>
FTP: Unknown
Verified: 15-Apr-94

sled@drebes.com
         (See the message below on how to use this server)

Public Key Ring also available from:
         ftp: alex.sp.cs.cmu.edu:/links/security/pubring.pgp
```

==

```
From: bal@zurich.ai.mit.edu (Brian A. LaMacchia)
Newsgroups: alt.security.pgp
Subject: Announcing WWW access to public keyserver on
      martigny.ai.mit.edu
Date: 22 Jan 94 00:19:37

Announcing a new way to access public keyservers...
```

The public keyserver running on martigny.ai.mit.edu may now be accessed via a World Wide Web client with forms support (such as Mosaic). In your favorite WWW client, open the following URL to start:

```
   http://martigny.ai.mit.edu/~bal/pks-toplev.html
```

Access to keys on the server is immediate. You can also submit new keys and/or signatures in ASCII-armored format to the server. New keys are processed every 10 minutes (along with server requests that arrive by e- mail).

The martigny.ai.mit.edu keyserver currently syncs directly with these other keyservers:

```
pgp-public-keys@demon.co.uk
pgp-public-keys@pgp.ox.ac.uk
pgp-public-keys@ext221.sra.co.jp
pgp-public-keys@kub.nl
```

NOTE! This service is experimental, and has limited options at present. I expect to be making changes to the server over the next few weeks to make it more useful. I would appreciate any bug reports, comments or suggestions you might have.

```
—Brian LaMacchia
bal@martigny.ai.mit.edu
public-key-server-request@martigny.ai.mit.edu
```

15.3 STABLE LARGE EMAIL DATABASE (SLED)

There is one public key directory that does provide authenticated keys. SLED (Stable Large Email Database) is an on-line service that includes repository of PGP public keys. Public keys in the directory are signed by SLED indicating that the user's authenticity has been verified.

The procedure for joining SLED is to mail an application form with the modest fee (At the time of publication, a $10 sign-up fee plus a $5 annual fee). To aid in verifying identification, payment must be made with a preprinted personal check with a name that matches the name to be placed in the user's directory listing. Payment must also be accompanied by a copy of the applicant's driver's license or passport. Finally, you must include your PGP fingerprint on the form.

Once your check has cleared, SLED will initiate an e-mail exchange of public keys and will return to you a copy of your key signed by SLED. Thus, for PGP users, SLED servers two purposes:

- It is a repository of public keys that have been signed by SLED.
- Your key gains the SLED signature, which should carry some weight with those familiar with the service.

Anyone with Internet e-mail access (not just SLED members) can send e-mail to info@Four11.com and will be sent simple instructions on how to obtain someone's key by e-mail or World Wide Web (WWW), and how to join SLED.

Index

PGP Message/File Processing Commands

Function	Command
encrypt a plaintext file with the recipient's public key	pgp -e *filename her_userid*
sign a plaintext file with your secret key	pgp -s *filename* [-u *your_userid*]
sign a plaintext file with your secret key, and then encrypt it with the recipient's public key	pgp -es *filename her_userid* [-u *your_userid*]
sign a plaintext file with your secret key, then encrypt it with the recipient's public key, and produce ASCII armor output	pgp -esa *filename her_userid* [-u *your_userid*]
sign a plaintext ASCII text file with your secret key, and then encrypt it with the recipient's public key	pgp -est *filename her_userid* [-u *your_userid*]
sign a plaintext ASCII text file with your secret key, then encrypt it with the recipient's public key, and produce ASCII armor output	pgp -esta *filename her_userid* [-u *your_userid*]
encrypt a message for any number of multiple recipients	pgp -e *filename userid1 userid2 userid3*
encrypt a plaintext file with just conventional cryptography	pgp -c *filename*
decrypt an encrypted file, or to check the signature integrity of a signed file	pgp *ciphertextfilename*.pgp [-o *plaintextfilename*]
create an ASCII-armored file, without signing and without encrypting	pgp -a *filename*